From Recovery to Emancipation
Stories of Hope

Edited by
Marion Aslan

"Hope is not blind optimism. It's not ignoring the enormity of the task ahead, or the roadblocks that stand in our path. It's not sitting on the sidelines or shirking from a fight. Hope is that thing inside us that insists, despite all the evidence to the contrary, that something better awaits us if we have the courage to reach for it, work for it, and fight for it."

Barack Obama

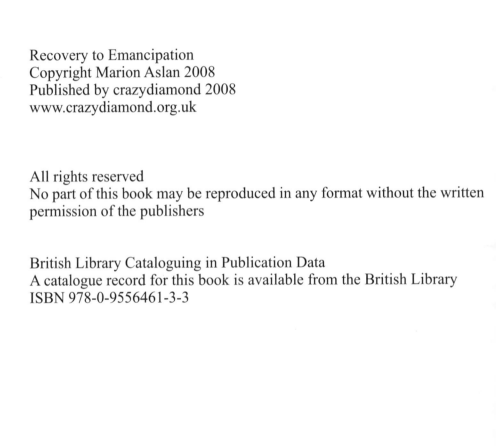

British Library Cataloguing in Publication Data
A catalogue record for this book is available from the British Library
ISBN 978-0-9556461-3-3

Cover photograph "Metamorphosis" by Olga Runciman

Printed and bound in England by Clifford Press Ltd, Coventry

Introduction

Many people who have experienced mental health problems can often feel alienated, disconnected from other people and lonely in that period of mental distress, but increasingly it seems that some can often feel equally alienated in recovery. There are still many detractors who deny recovery - statements such as "You must have been misdiagnosed", "You can't have been that ill in the first place", "You're not like the clients I work with, they're *really ill*" and "Well, you were lucky" are some of the comments frequently hurled at those who move on in life and totally reject a psychiatric definition of their distress. Carers, family and friends too can contribute to this rejection of total recovery without even realising it - well intended but overprotective comments such as "You're doing too much, you'll end up ill again" or "You should keep taking the pills, you need them" serve to diminish the huge journey of recovery undertaken by the individual and buy into the medical theories.

There is still an assumption that recovery is only for a chosen few. It's also still an all too prevalent view that people are not recovered - they are simply in remission! Although some workers and carers take this view, it is a view often espoused by users of mental health services themselves who reject the concept of recovery and cling to a maintenance model, often through fear and acceptance - fear of "letting go" of support from services, fear of taking responsibility and acceptance that the professional knows best.

Within mental health services also exists fear and acceptance - fear of taking considered risks to help move people on, fear of challenging clients to take more responsibility and acceptance that medical treatment is a necessity. Sometimes there may be a reluctance to do anything that "rocks the boat" because there is a very real fear of punishment from managers for doing anything different whatsoever.

Recovery, then, becomes assimilated into a predominantly medical model. Tokenism - that practice of making only a symbolic effort at something, especially in order to meet the minimum requirements of the law, pervades

3

our society in many ways, but nowhere is it more evident than in the sphere of mental health. Many people do recover - with or without help from mental health services, (and sometimes despite them) and the elements of recovery are well documented, yet few organisations are brave enough to fully embrace them. An encouraging realisation should be the fact that many of those who have researched and written about recovery or spoken about it from personal experience state the same process and elements necessary, even if there are slight variations in the language used. Yet, most services are resigned to maintaining or being maintained in illness rather than taking up the challenge of freedom.

There seems at the moment to be two polemic warring factions developing from this stance - not the traditional stereotypes of service users versus practitioners, as in that field alliances between the two do seem to be evolving, but within the group of service users, ex- service users, survivors and thrivers come these factions - the politically naïve infantry serving certain masters and the psycho-warriors. On the one hand there are the "happy to be patronised, play the game and get the rich pickings" category of service user. Turn up to the odd meeting, get paid just to be there, sing from the hymn sheet given to you and allow the master to tick his box of inclusion. They often buy into the stereotypes of the mentally ill pronounced by their professional puppeteers and rarely look beyond diagnosis, medication and maintenance.

The concept of thriving is an altogether alien one when one buys into the above model. Although they are often a voice for service users do these representatives actually speak the truth? Have they truly "been there" and risen, like the phoenix from the ashes of despair? I often listen to this group of user-professionals and wonder if they have dreams and aspirations for themselves, let alone the people they claim to represent.

...... but then, thankfully there are the fighters - the people who have worked hard for their recovery and either battled a way out of or side-stepped the system. If you feel I'm being harsh, consider this. What other branch of medicine, except perhaps recovering Cancer patients, has a group of people who refer to themselves as "Survivors?" Having worked in a variety of settings since my own recovery from distress, I regularly meet people who I am totally in awe of for surviving not only desperately difficult life traumas but also situations where the psychiatric system has crushed

4

them further. To survive and thrive they have had to fight back - against labelling and its assumptions, low expectations (from others and self) and sometimes from coercive treatment. These are the people often regarded as "difficult", "Manipulative" "Borderline Personality- Disordered." Or are they Psycho- warriors - individuals, with a retained sense of self and spirit which no system can crush?

"I value the term psycho- warrior; it describes people who are angry and fighting back, the Nathaniel Lees of our world."
Mike Smith, 2005

"They said I was mad, I said they were mad, and damn them they outvoted me!"
Nathaniel Lee 1653-1692

This book is a combination of stories, reflections and comment from some such psycho-warriors, people who have risen to the challenge of recovery but then wanted more, not just for themselves but for others caught up in a system which allocates labels and illness constructs to those in distress. These are the people I call the "thrivers". Thrivers have not succumbed to distress; they have survived it and gone on to emancipate themselves. Their battle is a much bigger one. They don't want others to be assimilated into the singularly medical regime they have encountered, so educate, inform and speak out loudly against such corruption of distress. They are the true experts by experience on recovery and thriving. Often these people are sidelined by mainstream psychiatry as what they have to say can be uncomfortable to acknowledge. By asserting that mental distress often results from appalling life circumstances for which medication is not the answer long term, it gives rise to the challenge - "How else can you help me!" As indicated in these narratives, there is actually quite a lot we can do to aid recovery, but it requires a very different mindset to achieve this.

"The real voyage of discovery consists not in seeing new landscapes but in having new eyes"
Marcel Proust

There are also stories in this collection from several people who managed either to avoid the system completely or who have elected to work for change from within the system. They have turned a negative situation into

5

a hopeful, positive one by using the knowledge and perspective gained from their own distress to give hope and inspiration to others.

Why do some people manage to look deep into an abyss, go to the darkest places and yet still reclaim their lives and move beyond mere recovery, whilst others succumb, are maintained or defined by psychiatry and its labels, drugs (the ones you don't get arrested for!) and power imbalances? In this collection of stories of hope, common themes emerge. The following chapters are personal narratives of the various components set out in "The THRIVE© Approach to Wellness" *(Aslan & Smith 2008)*, signifying how a range of individuals view their recovery or that of their clients with regard to these influencing factors. This book tells the stories of some of those who have overcome mental ill health, gone on to thrive and emancipated themselves. There are narratives and perspectives from those who have supported individuals in this way and those who have the vision that services could do things very differently if we dared rise to the challenge. Their stories are very different, each as powerful as the others, but in reclaiming their lives the contributors share a common bond.

Some of the contributors like Olga, Louise and Vanessa have had personal experience of the psychiatric system. Unfortunately that experience was more negative than positive so they have had to build up their own resilience strategies and learn for themselves how to move on. Olga, who uniquely became a client of the same system she was educated in and had worked for speaks of how power and patriarchy frequently lures the client into accepting a false freedom. Jennie dipped into so called "helping services" at a young age and could so easily have become a victim in adulthood of the system but rejected that route. Her strength and determination made her a survivor. For Mary, a "survivor mission" of helping others within psychiatry as an expert by experience has enabled her journey of recovery. One worker was a turning point in Guy's recovery, and as we so frequently hear, a Hearing Voices self help group gave him some of the necessary tools and strategies for recovery.

Mandy was able to emancipate herself after years of abuse living with an alcoholic husband thanks to good support from women's services. Bethany writes from the perspective of a young woman affected by the psychic distress of her mother and both of them having to reclaim and recover their lives. Daniel gives a brutally honest insight into the difficulties of his family life, and the emotional abuse which left him feeling worthless and confused, though he didn't recognise this till many years later. His recovery was aided by drawing on his innate resilience and learning more about himself and others who have been to the darkest of places yet who retained a perspective and even a sense of humour about the experience. In his chapter, Dr Mike Radford recently retired from his post as consultant psychiatrist in South Birmingham writes of the need for services to move away from states of fearfulness to those which offer relationships based on mutuality before we can assist the process of emancipation.

A common theme which seems to emerge is that reclaiming one's life is often done much more easily and quickly when the mental health system doesn't interfere or dictate! All that is necessary, in the words of Florence Nightingale, is to "put people in the safest position and let them recover". These are people who have thrived either despite or without intervention by "the system" and who have embraced emancipation. Their stories are individual yet they are also the stories of millions of people around the world - not mad, not crazy, not even ill - just players in the game of life who have found different ways of coping with the cards they were dealt.

Psychiatry's frequent insistence that individuals such as these are biochemically ill is a travesty. In many cases it is the perpetrators who caused the distress who are the deviants - a common theme emerging from those diagnosed with Borderline Personality Disorder is one of sexual / psychological/ physical abuse or neglect. By sweeping acts of human degradation under the carpet of psychiatric labelling, psychiatry is a willing partner in the humiliation of mankind. It is time that those involved in the "lucrative profession of misery" were brave enough to acknowledge that they have been wrong to attribute illness to a singularly medical cause and not only listen to but respond to the narratives of their clients.

The authors of the narratives in this anthology have moved on in their lives - way beyond recovery, to a point of emancipation, a place of thriving. They have been brave enough to hold the mirror up to their own lives. How many of us have taken that leap of courage?

"Thriving occurs when people regard themselves differently - when they see themselves as survivors or victors and no longer define themselves as clients, patients or victims. This requires honesty in recognising and

accepting various aspects of self - self knowledge, self acceptance, self determination and self worth. Most importantly there is huge freedom in being proud to say "I am who I am" - taking pride in having undertaken the long journey to emancipation." (The Art of Thriving, Aslan 2008)

Many common elements exist in the recovery journeys people take - not least that it's hard work! Similarly to struggling up a hill or a mountain, it is only when you get to look back and admire the view that you know it was worth the climb...

"Many years ago, I climbed the mountains, even though it is forbidden. Things are not as they teach us; the world is hollow, and I have touched the sky"
From Star Trek

My sincere thanks go to all the contributors in this book who were brave enough not just to have undertaken their own difficult journey and climbed the mountain, but for the honesty and insights they have so generously shared.
Marion Aslan September 2008

Emancipation or not? - Olga Runciman
"If you want to change your life, you have got to participate!"

I was thinking about emancipation, what does it really mean?

I know what it means to me: it is freedom - to grow, to love, to live my life to its fullest potential, something I was once told was never to be. Well today I am free, I have love and I am living life to its fullest potential. I think back and remember that once upon a time I was being told that I would never get well and must accept that I had a serious illness which would be with me the rest of my life. Today I thrive. Once upon a time I was being told I would never have a job again and had the highest of pensions because I was deemed incapable of even the tiniest of jobs. Today I have my own business and am on the way to becoming a psychologist. Once upon a time I was being told I must take medication the rest of my life and to view that as my only true hope. Today I take no medication. Once upon a time I was being told that I was very fragile and will need support the rest of my life. Today I am emancipated.

So what brought about my emancipation? I had no choice - it was a matter of life or death and therefore to set myself free and change my life I had to reengage and participate in "me". I became the difficult patient who went her own way but that meant I found the hidden door out of madness into meaning and understanding freedom and love and ultimately to thrive. I have today a richness and a depth which would not have been possible if I had not gone down into the pits of darkness. What I thought of once as an unbearable burden turned out to be the greatest of gifts - for I have become whole.

I also had the unique opportunity to become a client of the very same system I was both educated in and worked for, for many years. Therefore I thought I would write a short and some might say harsh story from these two perspectives called "I don't feel well", and as they do in the movies, I too state here, if this has any similarity to reality it is purely coincidental.

9

A view from the staffroom	A view from room number two
A view from room number two I am taught that you are so fragile, that you have a chemical defect, that medication is the only solution - but is it? My friend has the same kind of problems as you but she isn't here, what's the difference why can't we just talk like I do with her? But no, you don't even have to wash or clean yourself here in the ward; you can dress in dirty clothes and up to a certain point smell. You can eat like there is no tomorrow, food flying everywhere, all is accepted in this, *weird* I whisper to myself, place because you are "insane". You just have to say those magic words *"I don't feel well"* which means, so I am told, that I must come with a pill.	*I don't feel well*, only nobody listens, offering drugs instead of a pair of ears. I feel oh so tired, so tired, I can hardly get out of bed and there is only that one bathroom for all of us here and I feel dirty but nobody notices so must be ok. The corridor stretches out and there is nothing to do, the highlight of the day, is when the food is brought up from the kitchen. Oh God *I don't feel* well only nobody hears.
You treat me like shit and call me names and I as a staff member must be professional - what does that really entail? - and use as my mantra "he is insane he can't help it he *doesn't feel well*". I meet at the appointed time but am let down by you, *"I didn't feel well, so I didn't come"* you say, and if I ask *"couldn't you tell me you weren't coming","* oh no" you say "I didn't feel well". I know I am doing something wrong, but I don't know what. I ask the others	*I don't feel well*, but now you are annoyed offering the pills you pretend to help, but you will not listen and in my frustration I shout at you, call you names, you are so perfect not a problem to your name. But I know that's not true, coz I heard you crying in the staffroom, but someone was there listening to you. Why isn't someone listening to me? You just smile, say it's ok, so distant I want to scream. You have made an appointment, but have you

but they don't agree, say I am good at my job, good in what way I wonder. Something is wrong with this system I'm in, I know it, I know it but what?

I am flummoxed with this double bind situation. On the one hand I have a job to keep. I am supposed to get you out of the system and back into life again, perhaps even make you better. However *I don't feel well* makes all, including me now, bow to the "laws of insanity" and all is forgiven, all is forgotten, the professional smile switches on, I offer you a pill and I leave you alone to wallow in your insanity in a world which, pardon me for saying so, is pretty insane too!

But is all forgotten? Is all forgiven? No it's not, you shout at me, hurt me with your words or, maybe even attack me and though I will get help from a system who takes that sort of thing very seriously, I will not forget, and maybe if it's too much I cannot not forgive, no matter what I have been taught. You let me down, promise to come, to do, to say, and yet every promise is broken *"because I didn't feel well"* you say, this **will** affect me. The professional smile will be in place on my face because that is my

bothered to hear if I want to come, you don't listen and I can't explain.

You said you would help me and I thought that was true, you and the others said when I came, just relax, you are in safe hands here, we know what to do for someone like you. But I don't believe that anymore and I feel so confused, you expect something from me only I don't know what and when I try to explain and say I don't feel well, you smile your fake smile, offer a pill and leave me alone, this place really *is* insane!

I feel so frustrated, so alone, nobody listens here, so I don't listen either. Sometimes I shout and yes I have even attacked you, which I know is wrong, but that is because I feel so powerless. I'm told I'm psychotic when really I just disagree. Most times now I just say, *"I don't feel well"* and leave it at that. But why do you leave me in this lurch, why don't you listen? Is my explanation, my understanding of my problems really so wrong?

mantra taught to me by the psychiatric system, but inside I too am only a person, filled with frustration over those four little words, which give you carte blanche and leaves me in the lurch.

Something is wrong, but now I know what. It's you, *you* don't want to get better and besides I don't believe you can, the psychiatric system is right I can see that now. I understand now why I need to distance myself from you. Your words *"I don't feel well"* I now take literally. I will with the support of the system help you, by taking over your life because you are after all chronically ill and I am normal. I will, as I have been taught, observe you, looking for signs that indicate your differences, highlight this illness, this defect you are born with. Of course *you don't feel well*, you have a disease schizophrenia no less, all of the symptoms indicate this, and I must help, I must take charge. *"He doesn't feel well and he is therefore not able to make judgments or decisions I will have to do that for him"* I say backed up by the psychiatrist." *You don't like my decision, I'm sorry about that but I now know, that with an illness like yours one of the symptoms is denying this disease"* and

I am trapped in a system which doesn't understand, nothing I say, nothing I do makes any difference. You say, when the doctor comes, *"he is very ill, needs more help, look at him, he can hardly communicate."* I say that's not true if only someone would listen, but I know I talk to deaf ears, for you are already deciding what's best. Occasionally glancing at me with their patronizing smiles, I know what they are thinking, poor him, he is not like us and thanking the lord that they are normal. A decision is made for my continued treatment, I don't agree and when I protest I am told with a smile it's for my own good, but I know it's not, I am afraid and all I can say is "I don't feel well".

so I will end saying, *"this is for your own good of course"*. I don't expect anything of you now, not even basic cleanliness, and no more will I be disappointed in your lack of responsibility, or your inability to keep your promises, or even to show respect because you are now reduced to that schizophrenic in room number two. **You**, yes you, will now be trapped in what once looked like an aphrodisiac of freedom but now you are drugged, your words are just noises, your actions just there to be controlled. I finally understand what psychiatry is about, now I know what they meant when they, a long time ago said I was good at my job...	Nobody expects anything of me, nobody even sees me, I am beginning to wonder if there isn't something seriously, seriously wrong with me after all? Sometimes they don't even say my name, just him who lives at the end of the corridor in room number two. I thought once I would get help, just relax they said, but now I can hardly get out of bed, trapped in this fog of drugs and hopelessness, so alone because now, not only am I not heard, but neither am I seen. Who am I, I don't know. Am I alive or am I the living dead? It feels like the latter, stuck like this in this void, oh God help me *I don't feel well...*

I was thinking when I was writing this short story, of those four words *"I didn't/don't feel well"*. All psychiatric patients, clients, users of the system can use them and have them readily available at their disposal. While those four little words can initially feel like total freedom, it is false. From the staff perspective it can at worst lead to burn out, but for you as the client the nails in your coffin of disempowerment will begin to be driven down quicker and quicker until in the end nobody believes in you and you too will cease to believe in yourself.

Why is it so easy to fall into that trap? Power. Power on many levels I truly believe plays a huge role. The psychiatric system by being extremely patriarchal in its way of being lulls many a client into an immediate sense of *I don't have to do anything my needs will be taken care of I can fall back on the pillow of psychiatry and relax.* This is necessary for many in a crisis situation. However, being the kind of system that psychiatry is, it does not freely give back power; *you* have to take it back. Many do not, many are lulled into this false sense of freedom because the pressures of responsibility are taken care of, many give up and become the role model psychiatric patients and the cycle of negative expectations continues. Nobody, after all, is expecting anything from an "insane" person...

Healing and the handling of uncertainty - Dr Michael Radford

When I discharged myself from the UK mental health system after forty years of dependency, I thought it would not be long before I would have to be recalled. I felt I was unable to escape. Not only had my economic survival been tied to its dictates, but also my existential meaning. When a person is inside an institution, they become a part of it and it becomes a part of them. This invasion of the soul is perhaps more subtle in a partial institution than in the total institutions described by Goffman.

My older daughter gave me a book for the Christmas before I retired from my role as a consultant psychiatrist attached to a community mental health team. It took me eight months before I finished reading it, and I cried hot and cold tears. Only then did I feel that I was fully beginning the recovery process. *Human Traces* is a story by Sebastian Foulkes (2002) about two committed people entering careers in mental health as alienists or 'mad-doctors' about one hundred years before I did. One had heard voices before starting his studies at Cambridge. The other had trained in France and studied with Charcot in Paris. He had an elder brother, Olivier, who was tormented by multiple voices and delusions and was unable consistently to hold together the boundaries of himself. Both wanted to understand and find cures for such people. One pursued biological researches and the other psychodynamic. Both felt at the end of their lives that they had totally failed. I felt identified with aspects of both.

The Englishman with his grand theory of the closeness of the origins of Olivier's disease with the genetic changes required to become fully human who was limited to pragmatic social measures; and the Frenchman for his attraction to the Viennese school in the hope of finding cures through listening and talking. They became partners in the old fashioned sense and set up a clinic which took some unfunded patients from the asylums. The Englishman became Olivier's doctor, but eventually he could bear his condition no longer and he killed himself.

The Englishman was given comfort by one of his patients before his entry into Alzheimer's disease. "What you did for me and Mary was something

15

wonderful. You took us from out that place. Do you remember it? ... It was a prison... If you are going to lose your memory, like you say you are, then the last thing you should know before you go is all the good you did. Maybe you didn't cure all the lunatics. Maybe no one ever will. Maybe there are some things that men will never know. And I will not let you tell yourself that you have failed because you didn't do what no man has ever done before or since."

After 100 years there is still no cure for Olivier's disease. There has been progress in anti-oppressive practice, but more needs to be done. Liberty is not free. There are new challenges to our powers of eternal vigilance. Clients feel trapped by clinicians; patients and other clinicians by consultant psychiatrists; clinicians and consultant psychiatrists by managers; managers by civil servants ; civil servants by politicians; politicians by public sentiment; public sentiment is manipulated by fear. Who invented the idea of 'modernisation' as a cure for unfocussed service development in a postmodernist age? Fear flourishes amid uncertainty and is fuelled by terrorism and 'the war on terror'. Uncertainty underpins the perceived breakdown in trust in public institutions and is not removed by the present set of responses (Onora O'Neil, 2002). Fear pervades the mental health system at present and fear prevents healing.

The current doctrine that patients must always be believed seems to be a transfer from attempts to improve the child protection services. Uncritical adoption towards adult clients of the mental health services however well intentioned is both irrational and infantilizing. The current explosion of accountability practices does not solve the problem of trust.

The application of science is crucial. But there are two ways of doing this. The prevailing idea that we should apply the established body of knowledge ('science') with ethics, commonsense and humanity is the mistake behind modernization. It ignores the question about 'Whose ethics' and it ignores Hume's problem about induction. And the political doctrine that truth is a function of repetition illustrates the danger of this discredited view of science. It shows our vulnerability to the lines taken by those with power in the system. Without a satisfactory solution to the problem of induction, we have no intellectual resistance to totalitarianism (Russell, 1946?) and patients have no protection against the arbitrary pronouncements of consultant psychiatrists.

16

The second way is to apply scientific method as the ways to create a new basis for trust. I once suggested that instead we should see ourselves as applying common sense, ethics and humanity with science (Radford, 1982). This view of 'the new professional ethics' was most clearly spelled out by Popper (1998?).

The third way of handling uncertainty is by arranging separation from the perceived sources of uncertainty, from the madness within by disassociation and from the madness without by the segregation of those seen as mentally ill. The discussion of a new mental health act in England and Wales gave rise to a recent rehearsal of this route. Both were themes in 'Human Traces' and were discussed in my chapter in the textbook of community mental health from the Birmingham course (Radford, 2000).

In order to move from recovery to emancipation, I believe it is necessary to move from the fear which has come to dominate the mental health services in the last ten years. Emancipation seems to me to entail faith, not in the sense of adherence to a set of beliefs but in the sense that John Macmurray analysed its use in the New Testament, as an attitude to life which transcends the rules of the old covenant. It is connected with the assertion that the invitation to friendship is to be the new basis for relationships that are to be based on trust and equality.

Recovery - Louise Pratt

Recovery for me happened when I was faced with too few options and it really was a time that I felt I had to 'go it alone'. I had lost faith in those people who were meant to be my saviours. Hope of a recovery was something that was rarely, if at all, reflected by my supporters, and this would inevitably lead to a life that was seen as having so many regrets, failure, loss and pain.

I see now that recovery is experienced in a similar way to a gambling stake. The time had come when I had lost, entirely, those things precious to me. Would I be prepared to take that one last gamble that would either cost me, ultimately, my life? Or was there always that one last slither of hope that I would hit the jackpot, which would mean my life could get back on track?

As I have started to write about recovery, I stop and wonder. Yes, it is true that I did recover, but this sounds very medical model in terminology, although to be honest it was the best word I had at the time. So what did really happen in terms of 'recovery'? Well I did get better, improve, get on with my new life, but this could never follow a rule, model, practice or theory. It was not something that others could do for me either. In fact day one in my quest for reclaiming control and my life began when no one cared any more how bad the bad days were because according to 'them' I always got better (at least till the next time anyway).

My chance of a cure rested for too many years within a medical doctrine, ruled by medication. It never seemed to be a factor that regardless of how high they were prepared to go with dosages or how many changes they made or what combinations of drugs I were prescribed, it didn't alter my situation. I suppose it was only myself who realised that there was only one option left to try that had not been tried before. It was to be the most significant decision that I took, to stop all my medication, after years of prolonged use and abuse.

This was to be the first step towards my emancipation from the system. It was a dramatic decision, and it was one that made me most vulnerable, including a few narrow escapes from re-entering the system. It was definitely the quickest route out of the system though, because it soon became apparent that the system was no longer prepared to support me as I rapidly became more animated and filled with emotions that had remained dormant for so long. I did not fit any criteria anymore for needing psychiatric services. I did feel rather sad that after all the time I had been involved so intensely with the services, they attached no importance to continuing in supporting me when my 'symptoms' had faded, but were replaced by so many other difficulties relating to readjustment.

In hindsight, being left alone and free was a blessing, as there was no more observation, monitoring or maintaining. I could learn slowly and surely that my spirit and desire to live on would be what did, and continues to be, where I'm heading. It did almost feel that the professionals were neither expecting it nor equipped for adequately dealing with me getting over it. In terms of gambling on wellness and recovery, I started with a small stake and I won a little, but I liked winning, so I gambled again. This time the reward was slightly bigger and I liked the way it made me feel. At this point people who were close to me started to panic and feared that this gambling was going to be too risky and perhaps I should slow down a bit. Taking these risks, however, was to be a big factor in my emotional freedom.

It starts by pushing hard at those barriers, and imagining and believing. Believing that you can work again, you can go out anywhere you chose, you can get in touch with those old friends, you can drive your car where you have never been before, you can make that telephone call and you can give your husband a cuddle without fearing it will lead to more!!!!!

I was confident that I was the one now that was in control and although I was always aware of the possibilities of losing, I now had the courage and determination to keep on taking these risks. I had belief that I could now be a winner and other people started to believe me. I did always have the realisation though, that one too many gambles could, once again, lead to big losses but this was my comfort and strength and it was what kept me gambling on these life chances.

Recovery started for me at a time when I felt that I had been failed, and all those things like hope and belief, had long been abandoned for a regime of

19

drugs, hospitalisation and prejudice. I think back to such times when all I had to rely on was a primal instinctive drive to survive.

I do believe that this was a starting point to recovery as I only had these basic personal characteristics to rely on. I felt that I had reached a point where my only two options left were either 'sink or swim'. Fortunately I decided to expand on my inner strength and in an almost perverse way; I wanted to prove to all those people who had dampened my soul and destroyed my belief and hope that I was going to survive.

I had always felt that I had only ever been thrown one lifeline when I was sinking and this was based around traditional medical model methods. Unfortunately no one ever taught me to swim. This allowed me to drown in a system that never actually healed me.

On reflection, recovery for me was about re-establishing equal relationships; I think this can only start when your confidence and self esteem starts to improve. For those who previously knew me, it was hard to get them to change their view of me, but I had to have a positive lead on this to influence their own doubt. As I had to start to knock down my own constructs of who I was now and who I had been, it was obvious, that they too would have to do likewise to come to their own new understanding of who I had become.

What helped most was having good friends, confidence, guts and determination with the view that it is ok to make mistakes, and to have the belief, that with the right support, you can achieve your goals. It's about acceptance that you can have bad days and it does not have to mean that you are on a downward spiral. It's about laughter and fun and a new zest for life; it's for living today, it's about dreams and aspirations but walking at a pace that you are comfortable with, surrounding yourself with people that you enjoy spending time with and those who hold hope for you and who believe in you.

My life now, well firstly it's so far removed from my past inner world that I often have to pinch myself to see if it's for real. How? The first thing that hits me is that the past has earned its place as just a distant memory. No more snatches of dark thoughts, flashbacks, despair and desperation. This was not only due to my distress, but also due to the effects of treatment, all in the name of care in the Twentieth Century. I can only now look back objectively and use my experiences in a positive light.

How else is my life better now? It feels like living in a world that I belong to, I realise I have had to work hard to prove my new existence and this is usually about other people's fears not just my own. I have regained recognised status again in society by saying 'I do this job', 'I belong to this group'; 'I believe in this' and 'this is my life'. I have had to learn to live, function, feel and believe again. I had to reconnect to those things and people that had not entered my inner world with me. I had to re-establish relationships that had been wounded by my isolation. I had to believe in myself when no one else did and I had to allow myself to experience relapses in a way that was now part of being well, with the knowledge that this was to be accepted to others and myself.

There was nothing to physically distinguish me as someone who was experiencing mental distress then, and now, there is nothing to show the world of my past experiences, but I live my life with new meaning and enthusiasm that shows in all I endeavour to do, with the people I meet and the actions I take, so that my legacy from the past can reflect my life with new meaning, and in every detail, to who I can now be.

In some ways my emancipation from mental illness and/or the system seemed an obvious thing to do and I ask myself why I could not have chosen this way out at anytime in my past? There may be a hundred and one answers to this question but I feel that dwelling on that could distort my progress. Whilst I accept my past and take some responsibility, I have the hope that I am now fully armoured for my existing and future life.

I think I always knew that it might be someone or something you may meet, maybe not today or tomorrow, but that would confirm to you that you have had, somewhere hidden inside of you, all you will ever need to overcome your difficulties. For me this strength started when my emotions started to spring up, like the hairs on your arms, when the medication could no longer dampen my spirit. These opportunities are there for us all to explore and I sincerely hope that everyone has the chance and belief in themselves not to rely purely on traditional medical model interventions.

Today I am at a place where I had once lost hope of ever being. I take part in all of those things that I had been led to believe were never going to be possible for me to engage in. I work, I have re-connected to my loved ones, and I do live a full and varied life. I would say 'against all the odds' but I have only returned to my life as I once remember it.

It was others, all those people who didn't see past the labels, diagnosis and difficulties that had lost the vision of who I was and who I could be again.

Listening to my father- Guy

At the age of five I started to hear a voice. He told me that he was my father and that it was my fault he died because he was lifting me up at the time (my father died when I was four months old). I believed this voice because I thought he was my father. This is the first thing he would say when I woke up and he repeated it throughout the day. Then he started to say "You don't deserve to live - you're worthless and you're wasting the air". After hearing this every day I started to feel guilty and thought that I had killed my father and taken him away from my family. He told me that my family hated me because I had killed him. I was scared and felt alone. I didn't understand what was happening and how to tell people what was happening so I kept it to myself thinking it would go away.

I started primary school at six years old. This was not a good time for me. The other kids thought I was a freak because I would walk around on my own talking to myself. They started to pick on me. Every time they saw me they would shout "Here comes the freak". They would spit on me, punch me, and push me into the lockers. One day I was having my lunch by a pond at school and one of the kids came up and pushed me in and all the other kids started laughing. I started to stay away from them and have my lunch round the back of the school. I would wait until they all went to class first so they wouldn't do anything. The voice would keep saying "You see. Everyone hates you, you're worthless". I just wanted him to leave me alone.

Six months before my eleventh birthday I tried black magic to get rid of him. I was starting secondary school and didn't want the same thing to happen. I got scared doing the spell and left without finishing it. A few days later Lofty (my voice) had gone. I started secondary school and I was excited. Everything was going well for the first week and then it all started again. I was sitting in class when the devil appeared. He said "You know why I'm here. You didn't keep your part of the deal and I'm here to collect what's mine". I freaked out and left and never went back to school after this. I started to see all this other stuff: white faces jumping off the wall at me, red eyes looking at me through my window. A black bird followed me around. The devil kept coming to me saying "It's time to pay". I sat in my bedroom in the dark so I could not see what was there. At the bottom of my bed there was an old man with long white hair and a black arm started to climb up my bed. I freaked out and left my house. Lofty came back and said "You are so useless. You can't do anything right, you couldn't even get rid of me. Just kill yourself, no-one will miss you. Everyone would be better off without you". This is when I started to self-harm; it took the pain away. Lofty started to tell me that my mum was trying to poison me every time I sat down to dinner, so eventually I stopped eating. I could not sleep as I was scared that my mum was going to hurt me. Every time I watched television I thought it was talking to me. The words would come up on the screen and tell me to kill myself and the images would jump out at me. I stopped watching it. Two black shadows followed me everywhere but I was not scared of them. They didn't say anything but stood by my side. It felt like they were there to help me.

At the age of twelve I started to take drugs. They made everything go away at first. They became my best friend and didn't ask for anything in return. I spent most of my time in the Botanic Gardens. This is where I met a girl, her boyfriend and his mates. She was the only friend I had. She told me she could see the black shadows and knew that I had done magic. I knew her for five years.

At the age of seventeen her boyfriend and his mates sexually abused me. Everything came crashing down after that. I stopped going out for the next ten years and started to self-harm badly. I didn't want to live. Lofty would tell me stuff about other people and what they were going to do to me. I tried to kill myself many times but it didn't work. Then I started to think that maybe he was right. "I am worthless and stupid and can't do anything right". So I just sat in my room away from everyone. I could not be around knives or razors because I would get images of me picking them up and ending it all. I stopped washing and shaving. All I did was sit in my room getting wasted. I didn't know what day or what date it was and I couldn't tell what was real and what wasn't.

When I was twenty-three I went to my GP because I was getting headaches. He took my blood pressure and knew from the results that I was on drugs. He asked me if I wanted to see someone about that. I said yes. I got an appointment and one week later started to see a drug counsellor. Once we got talking she said she would like me to see a psychiatrist so I agreed. I saw the psychiatrist and started to tell her parts of what was happening. She asked me if I would mind waiting for a bit and the next thing I knew I was being sectioned and I was sent to hospital. The doctor there just stuck me on tablets and no-one would explain to me what was happening. I spent 18 months there. None of the tablets worked. After 18 months I was let out for a week and then put into another hospital. I spent seven months there and the doctors and nurses didn't seem to care very much. I got out of this hospital for a few weeks and had to go back in for another seven weeks. I started to take drugs again because I was not getting any help. During this time I started to hear a second voice.

Eventually I got moved to an early intervention team. This is where my recovery really began, although at first I didn't care what they had to say as all I wanted was to die. Then I met an occupational therapist on the team who talked to me about the voices. I had to accept that they were there and try to live with them, but this didn't mean I had to believe what they said. For the first time I accepted the possibility that they might never go away. When I had done this things started to get better. I started to challenge the voices by looking for proof of what they were saying. Most of the time I could not find any real proof but thinking about it helped me understand that the voices were not always right. The process of talking to someone also helped me to start developing my trust in other people again. Then I got into meditation. This gave me a break from the voices without self-harming. The breaks started as 15 minutes and then got longer and longer. I started to feel better about myself and make plans for the future. I started to eat. I started to leave the house for the first time in years and then started going to a hearing voices group and a meditation class. The meditation class helped me to explore my thoughts and being in a group helped me to further develop trust in others. The hearing voices groups helped by showing me that there were other people who had the same experiences as me. During this time I began to think that the voices were coming from my own feelings of guilt about killing my father. Until then I had always thought that the voices were my deceased relatives speaking to me.

At the age of twenty-six I realised that the voice I had been hearing was not my father's and this changed everything. This confirmed my belief that it was never my father that I was hearing, just a male voice. Soon I had days where I did not hear the voice at all. Now he comes back when I get stressed but most of the time I don't hear him.

I'm working towards starting a photography business and hope to get involved in working in mental health, so that I can help people in the same position and show them that there is hope and that things can get better with a bit of work. Things can change. You have to believe that there is hope no matter what people say because there is, no matter how bad things are. This is what has kept me going. It's about accepting what is happening and dealing with it as it comes up and not blocking it out. Talking about it makes it easier to deal with.

The things that have helped me most have been learning to challenge what the voices were saying and keeping a journal. It helped me to tell my story to someone else. It helped me to have people who believed in me and my recovery -people who didn't treat me like I was ill or that there was something wrong with me. It helped focussing on my strengths and writing a strengths list which I developed over time.

I have started a photography course. I had done my A levels in photography as a teenager but had not been able to pursue it until now. Being involved in photography has made me feel like I can do something. I recently got third prize for a photo that I entered in a competition.

I'm going travelling. I have started getting out and about in London and then I'm going to Europe for a bit. I am planning to go to Thailand next year and hope to go to a meditation retreat.

Meditation and confronting my feelings has been a big step in my emancipation, as has learning to accept myself. I no longer see myself as ill or damaged but human. I don't think I'm stupid or worthless anymore. Now I see my "illness" as a reaction to my life experiences and my environment.

My advice to other voice hearers would be to firstly accept what is happening to you and talk to someone about it. You don't have to accept what the voices are saying.

Stressed, Traumatised and Bewitched - Bethany Bell

I left school in 1985 having, in my opinion at least, gained little from an overly academic education in a local comprehensive. I admit to having had very little interest in the subjects I studied and would add that I was further hindered in my school career because my mother was a teacher at my school and this had many implications for my progress. Without dwelling too much on the past (which I have fortunately largely forgotten) I would say that I was not the best student in the world!

I belong to a loving and close family and I am proud of the fact that my father and mother have remained together for 44 years (my God, how long is that!) This is despite - as I will explain later - a 12 year period of severe mental illness in the family, something which raised its ugly head when I was just 19 years of age. I had some serious growing up to do having been protected from the "slings and arrows of outrageous fortune" by this strong family for my entire life until that point. I have one sibling, a brother called Christopher who has always been my rock. We have always protected each other and we have always laughed together even during the time of adversity. Christopher is now 40 years of age. He is married to Heather and has one child, young Charlotte who is 9 years of age.

It is not my intention to dwell upon my childhood, suffice to say that it was generally a happy enough time. I would say that childhood for me lasted until I was nineteen - a long time! But, like all good things, it came to an end. For the next 12 years I was sucked in to something for which none of us - family or friends - was prepared. This was the development of a serious mental illness by my mother. This was caused by the stress of a working life that had become unbearable to her.

Her trauma became mine; it became my brother's and became my father's. From my point of view, it changed me from a happy-go-lucky person into an anxious person practically overnight. Life goes on, of course, but in our house it changed completely. This was in 1989 when I was just nineteen. From my point of view, I still had to get up each morning and go to work; I still had put in a full shift in a busy shop. Often, I came home tired

27

and had to start again trying to keep up standards in the house.

But, that's enough of that. It wasn't all bad. I developed new coping strategies and found comfort outside the immediate family circle. Sometimes, I was able to forget what was happening at home when I went on holidays abroad, when I passed my driving test, and when I found that I liked fast cars. They just got faster and faster! I had boy friends and eventually married - as girls do. And - again as girls do - I lived to regret this, stayed put for a year - more stress - and then moved on.

Talking about stress - I did it all. I married, divorced, sold my flat, bought a house and went into business for myself. I loved working for myself and being my own boss. My goal in another year or so is to open a shop again, but this time I would employ someone else to do the hard work of running it. This would leave me with an income and a chance to do what I really want to do and that is to become a counsellor.

1989 - 2001 were years of frantic activity as I tried to juggle my personal life, my life as a family carer and my professional life. What happened in 2001 - well my mother started to recover. Can you imagine what that was like for the rest of us? The relief was immense to my body and to my soul. We - as a family - could start to live again.

Maybe this is a good point at which to say that I have known great sadness, I have been stressed and traumatised, but I have survived. I have learned that everyone has issues in their lives. It is how we cope with them and move on that determine the kind of person we become and how we develop. Towards the latter part of my mother's illness - when I was about 29 years of age - I took up dancing as a spare time professional occupation. Dancing took me everywhere! In my fast car I went to outlandish places like Manchester, Newcastle, and Birmingham - everywhere - even to the Isle of Wight by air! I loved it - it was emancipation, a breath of fresh air and I found myself earning megabucks. I saved every penny I earned and ploughed my not inconsiderable earnings into my home.

But dancing, too, came to an end when I became too old at 34 and the cellulite appeared. Now was the time for another change. I had watched my mother start to grow again as a person as she recovered. Until I started writing it down, I never gave much thought to the fact that we witnessed a miracle. I know now that my mother was the victim of a system, a very powerful system which medicalised her distress and which drove her nearly into the ground.

What we, as a family, saw in 2001 was how she - now reduced to a pitiful five and a half stone - prevailed. The only way was up. She grasped the nettle and gradually pulled herself (and us) out of the mire. I say she did it herself, but on reflection think that there was someone who had always stood beside her, waiting for the re-emergence of that spark which we call 'the self'. We watched in amazement as she started to fight back by putting together a plan which included all those things that THRIVE(c) is about.(The THRIVE Approach to Wellness, Aslan & Smith)

I am proud that my mum did it, that she managed to re-frame what was a frightening journey. It took time to heal the issues she had around voice hearing and the terrors she felt when she re-lived in the deepest recesses of her mind the traumas of her life.

We were to watch in amazement as she built upon the resilience and creativity that she had been known for. In one fell swoop my mum shifted from victim to survivor and - once again - started to embrace life and rediscover her skills and strengths. I have said that she pulled herself and us out of the mire and, once more, I am part of a close-knit and complete family.

My mum found purpose in her life through her writing and in helping others. She now has hope for life and for living. And, finally, she has a voice once again through involvement in a hospital magazine, in an anti-stigma campaign and through activities related to the monitoring of the services in a hospital where she was once a patient. She is truly emancipated, fit in both body and mind.

My mother's experience not only changed her life, but also my life. I had marvelled at the strength of the mind to bring someone back to reality. In 2002, together, we both went on a course at the City's University about drug and alcohol misuse. This was the start of a new interest for me in helping those less fortunate than myself.

From my mother I have learned many things; not least of these is compassion. I became 'bewitched' by the thought of a future where I could use what I had learned in life to move into a new profession. This time, one that could last a lifetime. I became a student again in 2002 and began a journey of self-discovery which continues even now. The last two years of my life have been spent attending college, working full-time, studying and - from last September - working with children.

I cannot begin to say how much I have learned in terms of new skills which have contributed to a satisfying and growing sense of professional development. This has been enhanced through regular sessions of personal therapy by a Gestalt therapist who has helped me explore aspects of my personality and come to terms with the past and my relationships with others. I can nearly say 'No!' to people now.

I have said I am bewitched. I am bewitched by what I have learned and continue to learn about the 'isms' - for example, humanism and existentialism. I even read books that I don't have to read because I am now interested in learning for its own sake. Gone are the days when I was a school girl sitting bored to tears behind a desk.

I have discovered new aspects to my personality that I never dreamed I had. I have a growing awareness of self and with it a new belief in what I can achieve. When this course is finished I hope to move forward - whatever 'forward' is. I face the future with confidence.

I now know who I am.

Surviving Abuse- Mandy Weaver

When I first met my husband I was a happy go lucky type of person, always smiling and optimistic in my outlook. I noticed that he drank quite a bit, but coming from the Welsh Valley area I was used to this as most people I knew including my father drank. It wasn't long before I was drinking with him on a daily basis and making sure I had alcohol available for him when he visited me at my home.

After a while he decided he'd like to run his own Public House. By this time I was fed up with his drinking and misguidedly thought that if he had his own pub with alcohol literally available "on tap" then he would soon tire of this, as people do when working closely with a desirable product like chocoholics in a chocolate factory! How wrong could I be? The drinking became increasingly worse and arguments occurred on a regular basis because of this. I tried to reason with him and constantly nagged him about his drinking and behaviour but this made him angry and aggressive which led to physical abuse.

At first I thought it was a "one off" and tried not to think of my mother's wise words, "If he hits you once it will happen again" I forgave him and we "made up". It wasn't long before we had another row and if I argued back and tried to stand up for myself, he would hit me, punch me, sometimes kick me in the kidneys or drag me along the carpet where I received carpet burns and on one occasion he even twisted my arm behind my back and broke my collar bone. I would leave him or he would throw me out and I would go and stay with family or customers from the pub. I stopped counting how many times I left him after thirteen, but I stayed with him another three years after that and I estimate that I must have left him over fifty times.

I always forgave him; usually this took about three days, I hated him the first day, calmed down by the second, heard his voice saying it wouldn't happen again on the third, almost going weak at the knees, remembering when we first met and how "in love" I was, I would then go back to him thinking everything would be ok.

31

This pattern of behaviour lasted for six years, during which time I lost my self respect, self esteem and at times the desire to live. Every time he hit me I was shocked and then I'd remember all the other times and think how could I be so stupid and forgetful. This I believe now was self denial which played a big part in the "merry go round" that was my life at the time. I had lost my "bubbly" personality and became totally obsessed with my partner's life, ignoring my own needs and neglecting myself. He was addicted to alcohol and I was addicted to him!

The turning point came, when I moved back to Wales and bumped into an old school friend. It turned out that she was in a similar situation; her partner was an abusive drug abuser and she had sought refuge from Women's Aid on a number of occasions. Talking to someone else who understood the complexity of loving an abusive partner helped enormously and it was through this meeting that I found out about Alanon which is a fellowship for friends and family who have been affected by someone else's drinking.

I attended Alanon regularly, going to weekly meetings, learning to focus on myself as well as learning all about alcoholism. At first I didn't know how to focus on myself as it was easier to talk about my husband and how if he stopped drinking everything would be alright. I talked constantly about him and his problem and how it was affecting our lives. Other members at the meeting once asked me if I was angry, I realised at that moment that I didn't particularly feel angry, in fact I didn't feel anything at all; I was numb! After a while it began to "sink in" that I wasn't responsible for him or his drinking, but I was responsible for myself and I did have choices. I eventually accepted the fact that I did love this man but his behaviour was unacceptable and basically I had to "give him up".

I had picked up a leaflet from Women's Aid from the probation service (my husband was on a five month suspended prison sentence for drink driving) and kept it in my handbag. After yet another row, when I was told to leave or he'd get violent, I left my home with my sixteen month old daughter, got in the car and drove to the nearest telephone box (no mobile 'phones then!) and rang Women's Aid. I was taken to a refuge ten miles away and was told that I could stay there as long as I needed to. I was overcome with emotion when I heard this, as it made me feel wanted. I cried myself to sleep that night, knowing that there was no going back this time; it was like bereavement where the pain would only lessen with time.

32

I was housed by the local council six months later in a maisonette in the, not the most desirable of areas, but still I was grateful. I kept in touch with Women's Aid through a mother and toddler group they ran at the time and was surprised when they asked me if I'd like to join their management committee as secretary. I was terrified, I had no confidence and felt unable to perform the task of minute taking, but with some gentle persuasion and encouragement I agreed to do it. By doing the minutes I learnt all about the organisation and gradually became more confident. After about four years of being a volunteer and with my daughter now in school, it was suggested that I apply for a paid position that was advertised in another group, I plucked up the courage and managed to get an interview, but was not successful.

Over the next couple of years I applied for three or four other jobs with Women's Aid, but although I was getting more experience each time I failed to get the desired position, I was beginning to think that this work was not meant for me. It was after I started doing a business administration course arranged by the job centre that my luck finally began to change.

A job vacancy became available with Newport Women's Aid. I was reluctant at first to apply as I was enjoying the course I was doing, but I was prompted to do so by my course manager. I attended the interview and was totally myself. I convinced the panel that I was the right person for the job because of my past experiences and my commitment to pass on what I had learnt to others who were in the same or similar circumstances; I got the job!

My life was getting better! I eventually moved from my maisonette to a house and then took out a mortgage to buy it as I was now earning enough money. I have worked for Newport Women's Aid for the past thirteen years as a refuge co-ordinator and continue to help women and children in their time of crisis.

My husband died six years after we separated at the age of forty two. He did try to stop drinking several times but sadly he was one of the "unfortunate few who do not make it". My daughter is in university studying psychology and is doing well. I have learnt so much over the years, but mainly, I've learnt how to love myself as well as loving others and that no situation is really hopeless - there is help out there if you take that first step and asks for it, because "you're worth it".

Emancipation was a slow process for me as my captor was indeed myself! I felt I was a "prisoner of my own emotions" and to escape from this I needed to be around people who did not judge or criticise me, but who listened and above all cared for me unconditionally with quiet understanding. I found that gentle suggestions about my life and others pointing out that I did have choices, enabled me to "step back" and evaluate all that had been going on, thus breaking the seal of denial. Basically I started to love myself and acknowledge my positive attributes which led to me wanting to take care of me and look after my well being.

The first part which was the hardest took about nine months. During this time the barriers that I had surrounded myself with slowly came down making me aware of the situation I was in and the fantasy world that had become my reality. I really thought and believed that somehow everything would magically be alright soon, as I loved this man and we were going to be together forever, I did not want to change my life plan. Going into the refuge and physically taking myself away from the problem, helped enormously.

Although I still wanted to be with him I knew I had to secure a home for my child. I still had a hidden agenda, though. I thought that once I got re-housed, maybe he would stop drinking and I would still have my "happy ever after" as the thought of giving him up for good would have been too much for me at that time.

A few weeks after I was housed I contacted him and he came for a weekend visit. I was so excited and full of anticipation of what the future might hold. He seemed sober when I spoke to him on the telephone (he was back living with his parents in Kent) I met him at the train station, but as soon as I saw him I was disappointed, I could see from his mannerisms on the platform struggling to put something in his rucksack, that he was once again drunk! I greeted him with false optimism trying not to show my real feelings and gave him a peck on the cheek. It became obvious very quickly that nothing had changed with him, but things had changed with me.

Being away from him for six months had changed me. As they say, only one person has to change and the pattern is broken. I could no longer go into denial and pretend that things were alright. He witnessed this and he wasn't as comfortable with the situation; he left a few days later and I think he was glad to go. A few months later when I was missing him again, there was a repeat visit and the same thing happened. It was really disappointing and part of me was sad that I was no longer in denial as this in some ways was easier. Another visit was to follow about six months later where he stayed for a week, but the final episode to the whole relationship ended when I no longer wanted to sleep with him; all in all it had been two years.

The part of the relationship that I didn't mention before was the sexual side, a part that is not normally mentioned through embarrassment etc. Well I have to say that sexual attraction between two people is a very powerful emotion and for me it was the first time I had experienced such a strong physical attraction. Looking back I think that it played a large part in the whole relationship from beginning to end.

I felt sad and not angry when it was over and still had compassion for this man that I had loved so much. I still cry when a certain song comes on the radio or someone says something to remind me of what might have been, but I don't regret meeting him, as I have learnt so much about myself and am now able to help others when they find themselves in the same or similar situations. And I still have hope in my life.

Unfortunately we cannot dictate who we fall in love with; however; we do have options - one of them being, we can "give him up" just like the alcoholic has the option to stop drinking; we can stop living in an abusive relationship, even if we still love the person. Like when somebody dies, it's not easy, but after a bereavement period we are free to love again; we don't forget but we do move on.....

We are not born walking - Jennifer Stensland

Childline had not long started when I first made a call to them. I remember Esther Rantzen all over the media talking about how it would work. To me, the publicity around at the time was the turning point, as here was someone willing to talk and to listen to something that was once regarded as taboo within society. But all they succeeded in doing for me was encouraging me to seek some form of medical intervention in the shape of "happy pills". Childline introduced several "specialist" counsellor's who had experience of dealing with "victims" of childhood sexual abuse, who would be able to help me. Trouble was, none of them were based in Scotland: they were from Carlisle, Wales and Essex.

Calls and letters were exchanged, but to me this was fruitless, as although I'm quite a good letter writer, there are just some things that are difficult to record on paper...the raw emotion of my experience was met with the expected text book response; with the exception of one, who was to become a strong ally in due course.

My maternal mother found me a counsellor closer to home when I was 15. He was an American guy who ran courses in hypnotherapy from his house, (participants in the course were encouraged to do so naked, as to work with nakedness, you first had to be comfortable with your own). For £15 an hour, he would sit and listen to me...argue with him.

In our first session, he conducted it with me and my maternal mother present, as he felt we had issues that needed to be discussed before we moved any further. In this meeting, he told me he was physically abused by his brother, so he knew how I felt and that I would get over it in time. My bruising was no different from his!!! I did at some point get up and walk out, with my mum following me. She wanted me to go back in, which I did, on the proviso that she never attended another session with me. I took to calling him Rick the Prick after that session.

These weekly meetings continued with him for several months. In one of our other sessions, he introduced me to a tape recorder. It contained a tape recording of someone playing heavy drum / jungle music. Rick explained; this tape lasts for 1 hour. The tape would play for 15 minutes and then break, then for another 15 minutes and then break and so on for an hour. During the 15 minutes of play, I was to vomit, spit and perform toilet needs or whatever I chose. The last 15 minutes of the tape was my reflective time! He said that this was a way to release my anger.

I was then taught breathing exercises by one of his assistants. This required me lying on a massage table, with his assistant placing one hand on my abdomen and one hand on my rib cage. This would be followed by her saying, "In thru the nose and out thru the mouth", while moving her hands in rhythm to her speech.

During this time, I was also introduced to two women from the local Rape Crisis Centre. I will call them Fran and Anna, as that was who they reminded me of...If my memory serves me right, I think I only saw them 2 or 3 times. But I do clearly remember my first meeting with them both. They came in with their lip service and mission statement ready to fix me. I questioned why they had come to see me as I wasn't raped. They explained that rape was the same as sexual abuse and that the effects were just the same. I know I was only 15, but I was far from stupid.

Personally for me, and no offence to anyone who has ever experienced such a terrible crime as rape, my abuse was continual rape...I wasn't abused once and left to get on with the trauma that rape brings. I was repeatedly raped...night after night and where possible, day after day. I was no sooner getting over one experience; I had to deal with another. Abuse and rape come from the same thread, but can both produce different garments that we wear through our lives.

As I moved towards my 16th birthday, Rick the Prick and Fran and Anna were gone; I still had contact with my social worker, who would meet with me when she could. There was an awful lot of stuff going on for me around this time and I knew I needed some serious help, as I was already on the road to coming to the attention of the Police. I had maintained strong links with one of the specialist counsellors that Childline had put me in touch with.

She had invited me to come take some time out with her and her family, which I did. This was really good for me, as it took me out of my world, away from all that was familiar and away from a place where everyone knew my name. I trusted this woman immensely and I would say, the first of all those I had spoken to up until that point, who I actually felt at ease with. There was no fancy jargon or lip service. There was no clock watching or someone telling me they knew how I felt.

I knew myself that this was only good for as long as it lasted, as I always had to come home, back to Scotland. So I looked for someone closer to home. That's when I tried the NSPCC. The counsellor I was allocated was good. She was young, so there was not the mother figure syndrome, which I felt with my last counsellor due to her age although the down side to this was that I could not help but compare myself to her. How her life was and how mine could have been. What I liked about this style of counselling was that she encouraged me to interpret my feelings in art form. She very kindly gave me a good pack of ink makers and an A3 pad and all the time I needed.

I fell pregnant not long before my 18th birthday. This threw up a tremendous amount of issues for me and not just about how do I make up a feed or change a nappy...more along the lines of would I abuse my son, would I beat my son or would I give him away. This was a dangerous time for me, as I was in trouble with the Police due to my anger and bad habits...and also my resentment to authority. I had so much shit come up you would have thought I was a mobile sewer.

After my son was born, I suffered from post natal depression. I avoided at all costs going to see my doctor; due to my background of childhood sexual abuse, the belief was that I would abuse my son. As a result of this pre-conceived myth that all abused children abuse their own, I feared going to my doctor, as to do so, would only warrant unwanted attention from the social services. Although I was still in contact with my own social worker, I learned quickly that it's not about what I say, it's about the way others interpret what they hear...the term "Ethnomethodology" (Harold Garfinkel) springs to mind here. In addition, my abuser was also released from prison and making plans to return home. So I was already under close scrutiny by social services through no fault of my own, simply by association!!!

If you put a lid on a boiling pot, sooner or later, it's going to boil over...the breaking point came when I put my head through a window and I went to my GP and begged for help. Thankfully, she was one of the good guys (gals). Unlike my last GP who tried to prescribe something for me, she listened to what I was saying and heard my plea. I knew if she had not done anything for me that day, I would have either done something dramatic to myself, someone else, or my son. I was neither brave enough nor cowardly enough to do either.

My GP referred me to the local Sexual Abuse Clinic and I was told I had 10x1 hour sessions with a psychotherapist. She came in with her clip board and pen, sat down facing the clock and introduced herself. She told me I could talk about anything I wanted to and that she would take notes throughout the session. From the moment I got there, I did not like her, the room, the clip board; all of it, especially the large white remind you of school days clock. I used my first session well; I told jokes for 1 hour strong, while she took notes. She even stopped me halfway thru a joke to tell me the session was finished. Needless to say I never turned up the following week.

I was advised to go back and try to make the most of it. Each time I got into the swing of talking, she would tell me time was up and that we would pick up where we left off the following week. I felt I got absolutely nothing from these sessions, except that I did not want to go down that road or go back to the local mental health hospital and I thought if I had to come down this route again, I would end up in there.

In the year with no counselling, I hit self destruct - sexual promiscuity, alcohol abuse and drug abuse. My relationship with my son's father broke down, I was confused about my sexuality and so far removed from myself that I no longer knew who I was or what I was. Then I turned 21. It was like someone had switched a light on. I knew that I had to get sorted, get out of the rut and walk another path.

I again went on the circuit seeking further assistance, this time opting to stay away from the more clinical route. I found a group that was Urban Aid Funded and worked at a grass route level. This group was started by a couple of disillusioned social workers, and it showed. Their style and techniques of therapy hit upon nerves with all of us. We all went in there like wide eyed scared lambs.

The thing with this group was it was never so much about what they said; it was about what they didn't say. They never told us they knew how we felt, how we were feeling, why we were feeling what we were feeling and more importantly, they never self disclosed, even when asked. They said that they were listening to us as one woman to another and that them either being or not being abused did not change how they treated or viewed us.

With them, I had Group Therapy for a year and then One to One Counselling for a year. The group was great because it let me hear for the first time, that there were more like me...I was not alone. We shared our stories and cried our tears without being judged or judging. We shared survival techniques, escapism tactics and more importantly, our dreams and aspirations for a future where our abuse was not the most important thing that had happened to us...it will always be there, it's just about finding more positive ways of coping, and we were able to do that with each other.

At this group, I made good friends with two people. One of them gave me an interesting book to read, and in it was a chapter called "Life or Death". Having read this where it talks about making conscious choices about leaving this world or remaining, I literally tripped upon an idea...I began to dabble in LSD. Obviously not one of my better ideas, but it was the more scenic route to take!!!

I was so far removed from myself that I no longer felt alive...I was dead from the neck down. I had to get back into me if I were to live. I realised that if I were to continue down this road of self destruction, I was keeping myself a victim. I was still being abused only this time, I was my own perpetrator.

The LSD allowed me to get back in touch with myself; it was a period of introspection. You know how when you are doing your laundry, you pair the socks together. You take one in each hand and fold them into one and other to form a ball. When I took my first LSD that was the effect it had on me...it was as if, all my emotions were on the outside and all the hardness and adopted survival techniques were on the inside. I would never advocate the usage of this drug; however, for me it worked. It was either self medicate with something grown from the soil or take some man made product like Largactil and have the feelings that were needing addressed

40

suppressed, therefore making me a slave to the pharmaceutical giants that hinder our natural right to heal free from their domain.

When the group was ending, I requested one to one counselling, as I felt if it all stopped now, I would lapse. Here I was able to carry on where I left off in the group...even though I had spoke within the group, I still felt in some way disconnected...almost as if I was talking about a little girl who lived down the road from me. It was not until I began looking at the abuse in its entirety and then breaking it down again without the constraints of the abuse, that I finally knew that I would never look back. I have always believed that if you don't go within, you go without.

This period in my life, free from medicine, was the most important thing in my life...next to my son being born.

I finished with this one to one when I was 24. I felt that I was able to finally move on with my life without their support...it also helped because I had changed my social networks. My life was good and I felt more than able to become a more productive member of our society...based on my past; the most appropriate work for me to go into was "care". Working with all the alcoholics, drug addicts, paedophiles, wife beaters and the rest that society regard as scum, is bound to bring up some issues...which it did. However this time it was different. It was to my advantage, I had insider information; I was raised by an alcoholic, wife beating paedophile of a step-father in absolute poverty.

When I was 29, I moved down South and continued working in the care field. Although this period spent down South was one of the lowest times in my life, it was also one of the best; when you're that low, there is only one way to go...the best revenge, is success.

I met someone when I was 31; this relationship was fraught with Domestic Violence. This coupled with bullying at work from Senior Management caused me to have a breakdown. I left my job and for about 4 months, my son held me together. He would wake me up in the morning and I would lie on the couch, and then when it was time for bed, he would wake me up from the couch and I would go to bed. I was drinking an absurd amount of alcohol; I had lost a lot of weight and accepted medical assistance in the form of anti-depressants.

41

These just made the blackness blacker. I had no motivation, my deranged ex was sitting outside my property watching me, phoning me, making and breaking promises. My son was being bullied at school because he was Scottish...we were no longer happy. I did what I do best, I upped sticks and went back to Scotland...and left my prescription in the bin along with the contents of my flat.

A little bit older and more the wiser, I again engaged in counselling. I am happy to say that it was not directly about the abuse...it was about how the abuse permits us to tolerate things that we would not normally tolerate and how we minimise what does happen to us. Like I said before, if you don't go within, you go without. Learning to love myself is the easy part, staying in love with myself is a life long journey.

I believe that we all have a falling out with society...and ourselves for that matter. How we become friends again is not about how many times you are sectioned under the Mental Health Act and how many prescribed drugs we can lay our hands on. For me it is about talking and listening...sharing and forgiving. Forgiving ourselves for beating ourselves up, forgiving ourselves for our failures, more often other people's failures.

We are not born walking.

My Story - Vanessa Al-Joudi

I was first abused at the age of seven. It was my seventh birthday - I had a party, a cake and everything. Only mum was working. So after the party I was sitting on the settee with my step dad. First he put his fingers inside me, and then he raped me. I remember it was eight o'clock at night and I was crying because I was so sore. He said I wasn't allowed to tell mum that I was hurting so I didn't. After that he raped me whenever he was drunk. He'd come home and into my bedroom. Sometimes he'd hide under the bed or in the wardrobe waiting for me. I still have the habit of looking under the beds, behind the settee. He used to make me watch porn which I hated and still hate now.

How did I cope? My mind wandered. I used to go into a trance. I used to hold a cardigan to comfort me whilst he was abusing me, I still take one to bed with me and hold onto it in times of stress. I was glue sniffing at seven years old. I didn't want to believe it was happening so I blocked it out any way I could. I only found out it wasn't normal though when I spoke to the girl who lived next door. I asked her if her dad got into bed with her. When she said no, I knew then it wasn't right so I kept it to myself until I was about eleven. I eventually went to mum then, though I think she knew all along what was happening. She just said, "Good, saves him having sex with me".

Our family doctor did have concerns when I was about eight and my periods started. He asked me about all the bruising but mum and dad were always with me and kept saying that I was harming myself, that I was a liar, that I was mad. My step dad was a bastard. He used to make me stand in a blue washing up bowl full of cold water as a punishment for any little thing. I still sometimes have panic attacks washing my hair. I hated the colour blue but I've made myself deliberately overcome that by choosing blue furnishings for my house, blue carpet, blue curtains.

I don't know why he only abused me as I had four sisters but I suppose they were never there. They were always off fortune telling. Later he got two of my brothers to abuse me with him as well. I don't hate them; I feel it wasn't

43

really their fault.On one occasion mum did actually phone Social Services to say he was raping me, but then she said she'd made it up because she was angry with him.

On one occasion he came home and I was playing with the only doll I had. I loved that doll but he was angry about something and chucked it in the fire. Then he cracked my head open with the poker and I needed stitches. They told them at the hospital that I'd fallen. When I came home he left me alone for a few weeks, then it started again.

When I was eleven I'd started to get cheeky. One time he came in and I said, "I've got you! I've got you in my pocket". Then I showed him this key ring of a monkey with a really ugly face. He went mad, snatched it from me and threw it on the fire. I was screaming at him, "I hate you, I hate you" over and over. He grabbed me, dragged me down to the cellar and started beating me with his belt. When mum came home apparently she found me collapsed on the cellar floor. I vaguely remember being taken to hospital in an ambulance. They admitted me and did some tests. They found out that I was four months pregnant.

From hospital I was sent to live with foster parents. I loved them and they loved me. I was so happy there. I stayed with them until I had the baby, a girl on 22nd December 1979. The baby was taken straight away for adoption and though my foster parents wanted desperately to adopt me I was made to go home. I kept saying I didn't want to, but mum was crying a lot and saying she missed me. I think she only wanted me home for the extra money it brought in.

The abuse continued. At fourteen my step dad made me bring a friend in to join in. I still feel guilty about that. Soon after that I started to prostitute myself. When I was fourteen I got pregnant again to a guy I knew and my son was born in December 1982. There was a case conference called because of my age and the baby was going to be taken off me. But my partner's mum arranged to take him with her to Jamaica and I was happy about that. I still see my son sometimes as he's back here now. His dad is in prison.

By September 1987 I was back living with my mum and my step dad. On this particular Saturday night I'd been arguing with my mum. When I went to bed that night we still hadn't made up. During the night I awoke to "see" her at the foot of my bed - she didn't speak, just kept shaking her head in sorrow and making a gesture with her hands as if to say no.

The following morning, I was in the kitchen and I thought I'd make amends by cooking for my mum. I can even remember what was on the radio - "Teardrops ... next time I'll be true" - Womack and Womack. Mum and my step dad didn't surface and eventually my brother went upstairs. He came down and told me to get up there, she was dead. I went up and found her, her head separated from her body. My brother was screaming. I just started laughing. I was laughing and laughing, I couldn't stop. I went to get some newspaper to clean up. There was shit everywhere.. But I was laughing hysterically too much to do it.

I ran to my sister's round the corner and told her about the body and how I'd tried to get the shit up. The police came. The doctor came. The house was sealed off. Five hours later the undertaker came. I was still laughing, I hadn't stopped. I was totally in shock. It was only when they brought the body down in a black bag that I started to break down and cry. I tried to grab the bag but they took her into a van and drove off. The police were all over the house, waiting to interview everyone.

Then my stepfather returned. He came in the back way. I grabbed a calor gas heater and threw it at him. It burnt his face and set the carpet alight. "Silly bitch" he said, "I should have killed you as well". I just grabbed a carving knife from the drawer and stabbed him. I kept on stabbing him, six times before the police dragged me off him. The fire brigade arrived. The police took me to the police station. I kept crying and told them, "I'm glad I've killed him."

I pleaded guilty when it went to court. When the judge sentenced me to four years I shouted at him, "I hope you choke on your breakfast, you fucking bastard". They sent me to Risley. I still remember my prison number. They took my clothes, made me shower and put on blue dungarees, black pumps. I didn't eat or drink for a week. The doctors gave me tablets and put me on the hospital wing.

After a month I was allowed to go to my mum's funeral. The governor came with me and I was handcuffed to her. She was good though. On the way there she let me take the cuffs off so I could go into a shop to get something for the funeral. We got to the house and the open coffin was in the parlour, the best room. I put the Black cat I'd bought (I remember it cost £35) on my mum's stomach. I was talking to her and I thought she was talking to me. I even thought I saw her move and I started to laugh again, so much that my brother slapped me. They wouldn't let me go in the funeral car; I had to go in the police car with the governor. It was a big gypsy funeral and all through the service I kept pushing down on the handcuffs trying to hurt myself. When we went out to the graveside I tried to jump in.

When we got back to Risley they said there was good news. The judge was to be in chambers soon and would be recommending two years in a probation house, one year in Rubery Hill mental hospital and a year in Cathexis, a home for abused women.

Some years later I met Nick and fell pregnant with my second son who was born in August 1991. Whilst I was in hospital Nick was busy spending my compensation which I'd received for a rape whilst in a Salvation Army hostel a few years earlier. He was drinking heavily and even trashed my house. So when I came out of hospital with my son we slept in a chute. During the day I'd go to a friend's house and she'd make up his bottles for me, let me bath him etc. This went on for several weeks.

I was still with Nick and one day we were sitting in a park with the baby in his pram. We were both drinking with loads of other alcoholics. I put a blanket over the pram, but the sun was so strong it caught the baby's face and he got sunburnt. I took him to the doctor, and he contacted the Social worker. The police were really good to me though. The Social worker had known I was sleeping rough and the police eventually pressurised her into finding me a placement, a mother and baby unit. Nick and I continued our relationship and I married him the following year and we moved to Derry, Ireland for six months. He drank a lot though and when we came back to England he started knocking me about and also hitting and abusing our son. I wasn't having that so I put him into temporary foster care to keep him safe.

I got divorced in 1993 and went to live with a friend, who helped me come off the prostitution. But by this time I was on hard drugs and in 1995, I de-

46

cided to put my son up for adoption. Nick was dead by this time. I met and married a Yemeni guy and in March 1995 my second daughter was born, followed by another son in March 1996 and then another daughter in February 1997. Whilst I was in the hospital with my last daughter two police officers arrived at my bed and announced that they wanted me to accompany them to the station. Her sister had been at nursery and bruising had been detected. The police were saying there were suspicions of sexual abuse as further examinations showed what looked like a hand mark near her vagina. Yusuf had said nothing about this when he came to visit, yet she had been taken away days earlier. My son had remained with his father. I was taken to the police station and a solicitor was called. I was told that my girl was in care. She never came home again, she was sent straight for adoption.

I had told Social Services previously that I felt uneasy about my partner getting into bed with Mary. He used to block me out, he fed her, changed her, did everything. At the time they said how good it was that he was bonding with her. But because I'd been abused I was always a bit suspicious. He kept promising that he hadn't abused her, that it was in my head. He was still saying that now, that it wasn't him but I didn't believe him. He was beating me and then in 1998 I found him in bed with one of my friends. I kicked him out but soon after I had a breakdown and ended up being sectioned in a psychiatric hospital.

Whilst I was in hospital my flat was destroyed by fire and as the two kids were with my ex he managed to obtain a residency order. On my discharge from hospital I wanted to sort out getting my kids back. But things went from bad to worse. I went out to the shops one morning and was shot at from a passing car. The police fortified my apartment, alarms through to the station, personal alarm to carry with me and then eventually arranged a move to a completely new area for me.

The children remained with my ex. I originally had contact twice a week, then that was cut to one day a week. He was granted permission to take the children out to the Yemen. It was meant to be for three months, but he stayed out there for six months, and when he returned he brought his new, young wife back with him. She came to my house once and there was an altercation. I admit I pulled her veil off, but she accused me of hitting her and I was arrested. It was thrown out of court thankfully.

Then one day, when the children were leaving after being with me, my son said "We won't be coming next week, mum 'cos our big sister's coming to see us". I couldn't believe it. No one had told me, but apparently my other daughter was coming back to live with my ex. I moved to stay with a friend during this time. I was mentally unwell and lost contact with the children.

Then there was a case conference and the courts agreed I could see the children again, It was arranged for me to have them in two weeks time for the weekend. The weekend before they were due, though, I was in bed watching T.V. when two Arab friends of my ex burst in. One held me down while the other raped me I had to have an operation because of the buggery. He got seven years in prison for that, the other one got two. I received compensation which I've asked them to defer. It's for the kids.

How have I coped? By "putting a gate up". By putting a "gate up you keep strong. It's like a slide inside my body - if I'm being abused the slide protects me. I often feel guilty though. Did I take the easy way out by killing him? I feel guilty I didn't protect my mum.

I sometimes feel like a little girl, like when I was being abused. I never had a childhood, not a proper one so I like to spoil myself sometimes. I like my baths, I have five or six a day! I treat myself to bubble bath. I was never allowed that as a child. I could only have one bath a month. I have to be clean. I don't like a mess. I have to keep checking things. You feel the need to get the "dirt" out of you, that's why I washed myself with bleach that time".

I think I'm resilient. I could sit here and take all my tablets and die. Or I could end up in a mental hospital going barmy. Why? Mental hospitals just make you more barmy!

I want to be in control of ME. I don't want to be a "cry for help", "poor Vanessa", I don't want to be a victim. I want to be Vanessa who's, yes, been abused, seen her mum murdered, seen all the shit. But I will never kill myself over anything, not even over my "mum" being murdered. I want to be strong, back in control and I'm learning to be.

A Survivor of Psychiatric Services - Mary Nettle

Firstly it seems astonishing to me that I have survived to the age of 54 (having been diagnosed with Bi-Polar Disorder and subject to treatment since 1978) relatively unscathed. Many things have happened to me along the way which would have made life hard going even without the struggles imposed by interventions from the psychiatric system.

Being incarcerated in the old fashioned asylums of the 70s and 80s cannot be good for anyone's mental health. The days of single en-suite rooms were at that time undreamt of, though admittedly are still not a reality for all even these days. I am still living with the impact of being diagnosed as mentally ill.

The stigma started immediately with the impact of my husband refusing to allow my family to visit as it might upset them. He would not have done this if I was being treated for a physical condition.

It was thought that one of the reasons for my mental health difficulties was the fact I was on the contraceptive pill, which was new at that time. As a Catholic and newly married, it was considered that we should start a family. The fact that we had decided not to have children and the fact that I was pursuing my career (I had a highly paid executive post in marketing research, which again was unusual for women at that time) made people assume that I was acting against my natural instincts.

I had entered the hospital because I had suffered stress at work which caused me to lose it big time. I had a hysterical breakdown in the workplace. I had a stressful journey to work in an unreliable car and many people at my level had been made redundant. I was pleased that had not happened to me, but on reflection it would have been better if it had, because what happened in fact was that my workload doubled. I always wish to give my best and when I was asked where promised work was I had a total breakdown there and then. I was crying, I was confused, didn't know what was happening to me. I couldn't tell the nurse at the factory any details about myself, not even my name.

After this I was collected by my husband, taken home and to an appointment with my G.P. He prescribed valium to calm me down. I'd never had this before and it rapidly turned me into a zombie. Eventually I received a home visit from a psychiatrist who suggested I need a rest in hospital, and in my zombie-like state I agreed to please my husband.

Going into hospital was an awful experience for my husband as well as me. Neither of us had any previous experience or knowledge of psychiatric hospitals. We were given directions but no information as to what the place was like. We had to go through a gate house surrounded by high stone walls. I was not in the main block but in a Nissan hut left over from the war. We had expected a brightly lit, warm, welcoming place as hospitals should be. This was certainly not it!

I ended up there for three months. During that time various medications had been tried, making me either very stiff or very floppy. No one spoke to me about the reasons for being there. I remember there were loads of cats living on the ward which affected me as I've discovered subsequently I am allergic to cats. There were only two records constantly being played - one of which was Johny Cash "Burning Wheels of Fire" and the Eagles, "Desperado."

I asked my psychiatrist if I had a diagnosis and he told me I wouldn't like it, but I had Manic Depression, would have to take Lithium for the rest of my life and it was like being diabetic. Thankfully I was chucked out as Christmas approached. The psychiatrist said he would see me in three months time at outpatients and that was it! From this rough beginning, it's amazing to me how and why I have survived. I feel it's due in part to two things; a genetic resilience which seems to be inbuilt in my family, particularly demonstrated by my mother's attitude of tough determination and in her case (but not mine) a strong faith. The second reason, maybe somewhat controversially is my decision to eventually embrace the psychiatric system by working within it to change it. I am not alone as a user survivor doing this. I work with many inspiring people, some of whom are far more radical than myself and who have somehow managed to escape the system.

I have tried many times to reject it myself, equating emancipation with being medication free. I have had long spells where I have managed to come off the Lithium completely, usually supported by my doctors to do

50

this, but following one episode of dissociation which frightened me considerably, and much pressure from family I have come to accept that on balance taking Lithium is not as harmful to me as I thought. I have over time come to cooperate with the system taking medication and other help to avoid hospitalisation. By doing this I feel that I have not sold out. I am just able to get the best out of what I am and what I do.

Looking back at my life I have this huge blank period when I was a passive recipient of services, living with my husband who was turning into a chronic alcoholic, who had as many problems as I did and sadly who never did recover. At the time I felt I was chemically enabled to cope with his alcoholism. I eventually found the strength to leave him and he died shortly afterwards. To me it felt like a slow suicide.

I got my self respect back by meeting people involved in national user organisations including Survivors Speak Out and Mindlink. Survivors Speak Out chair was a user survivor Peter Campbell, a very inspiring man who works as a writer and trainer (the organisation no longer exists). Mindlink is the service user voice within Mind the national mental health charity. I was involved with Mindlink from almost the beginning and was chair for a few years. Being involved in both organisations contributed greatly to me finding that I was resilient when I did not know it. I can not stress enough how important my fellow service users have been in making me aware of routes to emancipation and recovery that they have taken for themselves.

Emancipation for me has involved taking ownership of my experience and speaking out to change things not only for myself but for other people as well I feel appreciated and feel that what I do is worthwhile, giving me a purpose in life. The last ten years have shown me who I am and what I can do. I am self employed as a mental health user consultant. I work as a Mental Health Act Commissioner visiting people detained under the mental health act two days a month. I am very interested in user led /controlled research. I am proud and honoured to be the elected chair of ENUSP, the European Network of Users (ex) users and Survivors of Psychiatry and to earn a, small, living bringing about change in the world of mental health. Resilient, that's me, bring it on...........

Ugly Love - Daniel

My name is Daniel and I am 28. I am not diagnosed with having a "mental illness" but I fall under the rather broad and unspecific category of having been emotionally abused in family life, to a point where I did not realise I was being abused until recent years and I am only just realising how this has impacted upon every other aspect of my life. I believe that I have been raised in a set of circumstances that is genuinely unique, even in our times where the "dysfunctional family" is such a commonly used term.

I lived in a council house with a scrap heap just over the other side of the road. The cars looked beautiful all piled on top of each other with moss growing on parts of them. I remember the tarmac on my nursery road being dark red like a magic cherry cake. I also distinctly remember putting my Mother's cat in the washing machine. Luckily I didn't know how to switch it on at this point in time!

I don't remember very much from my early childhood but what I do remember is all rather happy. At the age of about four I do vaguely remember being with my Grandmother-a very kindly lady in her home. She was at the bottom of the stairs and I was at the top and as I walked down the stairs a very tall man walked past me. He didn't look very well and I had nothing to do with him but I knew there was some kind of link between him and myself. That man was my Father.

My Mum met and a couple of years later married a man that lived at the end of the street. We moved areas but within the same northern town. He quit his job in a food factory around the time he moved in with. A couple of steady years went by and life ticked along then one day I got back from school and was told I was going to have a brother or sister. Well that was good!

Then arguments began, mainly about money the ones I heard. He wouldn't work and my Mum went out cleaning factories for extra money. Things got worse he'd go out drinking when he was supposed to be food shopping. Then hours later he would return with no food and the money would be gone. Then a screaming argument would ensue on his return. There wasn't much money and I didn't go on holidays but I was happy. We lived on the top floor of a flat at this time- just over the road I could see my school playground and the playing field from the living room windowsill. One break my class friend asked me where I lived and I pointed to the top floor: "whoar-really?" he gasped with audible enthusiasm. Now if it had been the bottom floor I would not have got that kind of reaction!

My brother was born when I was 8 but I didn't want to hold him as I was scared of dropping my newborn brother on the hospital tiling. But I did after a bit of persuasion! Shortly after this time my Step Father went out with his friends and he didn't come back that night. I remember seeing something on the national news about a blaze in a factory in our town-I was allowed to stay up late that night as my Mother was waiting up for him.It was the only time I'd ever heard our town on national television and sure enough he never came back and the brief news story on the TV was about him-he was in prison for arson that had gone badly wrong, his friend, Ryan died.

I remember Ryan, as he was stopping over in our living room in the days leading up to before it happened. I was within earshot of hearing how he'd been dragged out of the flames still moaning before he passed away that night, I wasn't traumatised by hearing this-but it was strange nonetheless. I liked Ryan-he was very nice towards me. He slept in the living room in a sleeping bag. I woke him up one Saturday morning as I switched the television on for the early morning cartoons. He was ok about it and made a cup of tea. I'd get up extra early on the weekends for 6am-sometimes earlier! It's the direct opposite to how things are with me now!

Shortly after this happened we moved to a city in the midlands severing all ties with the now imprisoned stepfather. One day my Mother asked me if I wanted to see my real Father. I said "yes" so she went to a payphone to call direct enquiries giving the surname and address she then spoke to my Grandma. The conversation seemed to go quite well; she spent 50p so they must've been talking for a while. We then started walking back to the house and she said "...but your Dad is mentally ill". I then got a bumbling explanation of what mentally ill meant- "Sometimes he has to go to hospital, he takes medicine and sometimes he might not be able to see you because of this".

Then a while later I met my Grandmother and Father during the holidays. My Grandmother was in her seventies and was very well spoken-a lovely lady. I had a half-sister the same age as my brother but they had split up. Grandmother used to be a teacher. Grandfather died when my Father was seven. I know nothing about him aside from that he owned his own business, he was tall and wore glasses and I share his name.

Of course in the playground I'd missed out on the "my Dad's tougher than your Dad" arguments. Well now I had one and he was very tall and broad-probably the strongest Dad in the class. My school friends that saw him agreed with this. I went to see my Grandmother and Father during the holidays. It was really great as I got to know them and they got to know me. I was content with this arrangement even if I wanted to see them a bit more. My Mother couldn't work because the government didn't pay childcare fees at the time so I was raised on meal ticket vouchers and free milk at break until Maggie Thatcher stopped it! Money was sent every week in an envelope but after a time this became an increasing issue.

My Father's illness was noticeable in that he would take a lot of tablets-more than 20 per day. He'd shake his head and at times and his body would twitch. Mum told me it was because he'd had electric shock treatment. It sounded brutal and scary and of course it is. She'd take the piss out of him behind his back and get my little brother to mock him along with her when he was only 5. I've recently found out it was more likely Tardive dyskinesia-involuntary movements caused by exposure to antipsychotic drugs that caused this.

She'd call him "looney" and stuff when he wasn't there. It's not very nice having your Mother and little brother calling your Father a looney. Then when we fell out, I was told "You'll turn out like your Father in the looney bin". I took it on the chin and shut my bedroom door-couldn't really come back on that at the time.

Father never spoke about his illness to me but I'm sure he knew that I was of aware of it. My Grandma also never discussed it with me. So my only source of information was from my Mother and her understanding seemed at best on a par with the Victorian era.

Cracks started to appear after a while-when it was going so well my Mum would ask me: "who do you love the most me or him?" I told Mum I felt the same for both of them. She'd keep re-asking and slightly re-phrasing this until I realised the only way to change the subject was to tell my Mother it was her I loved the most but really it wasn't the way I saw it as a 9 or 10 year old. I mean you love both of your parents don't you?

I was also told stories about how when she was with him he used to exploit my Grandmother, conning her out of money and also about his drug use which involved needles. I was told how he used to punch my Mother in the stomach when she was pregnant with me. Frankly I don't see how I was to benefit from that kind of information particularly before I'd even got into my teens.

How did I feel about my Mother telling me "I'd end up in the looney bin"? Even at this young age I had to learn to switch off from this kind of stuff. I guess in hindsight it should have induced fear and paranoia. As an adult it surprises me that a parent could be so uninformed, ignorant and cruel about such an issue.

Cracks started to appear in the relationship as my Father increasingly failed to send the £10 a week keep. My half-sister started getting more keep which was a bone of contention with my Mother and understandably so. She'd say: "you can't keep a pet on ten pound a week". But she'd never say anything to him or my Grandmother. It went on for months until it was finally addressed.

Things took a steady decline with my visits up north to see my Father and Grandmother. I remember driving back with him in the car with him carrying a big bottle of cider in his hand as he drove down the motorway. He actually fell asleep at the wheel for a few seconds and I was about to tap him on the shoulder as I was sat up and undid my seat belt in the rear seat but he came back around just in time. I also clearly remember being around him in the mornings when I was staying over and the first thing he did was take a swig of alcohol. No two ways about it, he drank a lot and this became increasingly prominent!

I never knew what diagnosis he had I was just increasingly told that he was a "looney" by my Mum. Many years later my uncle told me that my Father was a paranoid schizophrenic and that he "completely lost it". My understanding is that he became unwell after I was born. I was given some accounts of this by my Mother but again they weren't very constructive as descriptions were given of his illness and even parts of his psychosis.

I hid his illness from my friends. I told them he was a security guard. It sounded about right - he didn't seem the type to be working in an office. As my brother got to the age of around four he was told that his Father was dead by Mother she seemingly attempted to protect my brother.

Mother established a full-time job with office work when I went to secondary school and a couple of years later then got involved with a man she'd met called Bill through a lonely hearts advert in the local paper. It was suggested that I stop seeing my Father at aged thirteen and I went with the idea. With the keep arriving inconsistently and the increasing drinking it seemed like he didn't care. Maybe Mum thought this guy would take better care of me and replace my Father.

Life with my step-Father was not without incident. I mean within a month they were arguing. They'd argue all the time! From the age of 13-17 I was living in an environment where there were arguments almost daily. When his kids came around every other Sunday there would be mayhem as my Mum clearly showed jealousy towards his children. It was dark. Then things got physical-but the thing was she'd be the one hitting him.

Bill took serious abuse from my Mother and he took it and kept coming back for more. She'd scratch his silver car with a set of keys, cut out the pockets in all his suits, throw away his shoes and leave scratch marks across his face. So he'd go into work in a pair of white trainers, a suit without pockets and a scratch across his face-I can only imagine what he told his colleagues at the supermarket that he managed. I even heard her say she'd urinated in his aftershave bottle once. This pre-dates the Jerry Springer show by several years otherwise it'd have probably been a featured.

The arguments, anger and fury were either directed at Bill or it was focused around me. If my Mother was falling out with Bill then I was the good guy. If Mother was arguing with me then I was the bad guy and Bill was relieved. If it sounds ridiculous then that's because it was and for only temporary moments was this unrelenting conflict ever absent.

The emphasis went back onto Bill and the more he took it the worse it got. It was savage and I believe very damaging to my younger brother. Mum told me that Bill's father had murdered his mother and then his father had killed himself when Bill was a child a couple of years into their relationship. Bill had one photo of his mother in black and white and I saw her rip it up into pieces. He almost cried then as she left him in the bedroom. He wanted to weep but he couldn't when he needed to. He'd have been wise to have packed-up long before things came to this.

Despite this and all the plate smashing that went with it my mother told her colleagues and friends that Bill was knocking her around. She'd be really rude over the phone to females he worked with and at one point convinced herself that he was cheating on her. She found out he was not by getting her work friend to follow him around in her car once.They eventually split after four years of this after another screaming argument that resulted in my Mother leaving to stay with a friend. She stayed there for two months and only came back to strip the house from top to bottom when she got a place of her own. She even took the fireplace.

While this went on I left school without any GCSE's and worked in Kwik Save for several years. I see this as quite a good time really as there was no end of banter in the store with the other workers and I became a little bit more outgoing and confident than at school. To be fair I had ambitions that I gradually worked towards as the thing I wanted at the time was to get a degree at university. It would put right my previous failures at secondary school and also provide the opportunity to live in a different city.

By the age of 22 I was packing my bags to live in Leeds to do a degree. I decided in my final year of the course to do some voluntary work as I had an inkling that I would prefer it to my market research job. I walked into a local charity and explained to the receptionist that I wanted to volunteer and by sheer coincidence the manager of the learning disabilities department was walking past and overheard what I was saying. I went to the interview thinking it was for a voluntary position and was told half way through that it would be paid work - cue laughter at the interview desk! The job was offered to me a couple of days later.

I enjoyed the work and straight away knew that I wanted to work with people. I found it more interesting, fulfilling and varied. After finishing my course I worked in a summer camp over in California for children with learning disabilities. I also stayed over there for a while and travelled around the West coast.

Things were really starting to take shape as I felt I was starting to get a good idea of what I wanted to do career wise. On returning to the UK I got a job in an acute psychiatric ward as a health care support worker. My reasoning at the time was to get as broad an experience as possible as I considered options about possibly being a healthcare professional.

The Incident

The incident was preceded by my brother getting back from a party almost four years ago. He'd had a few drinks and after clamming himself up emotionally for the last few years towards the rest of the family he told me in the living room that night that he knew his father was not dead but he had kept this from myself and Mother. He'd found this out three years before by listening to a tape recording that my mother had kept of a meeting with a "psychic" in which she'd openly discussed this and other things that were not discussed within the family.

This all made sense as there had been a significant change in his personality around the time he found this out when he was aged fourteen which was way above and beyond the usual territory of turning into an adolescent. He'd gone through my Mother's wardrobe out of curiosity as he knew about the tapes existence and wanted some information about the unanswered questions about his Father for which he'd been told had died but was never really spoken about. My brother spoke about how he had been affected and it might be described as quite a logical response and it is awful to imagine that someone could find out such a significant issue in such an undignified way. It left me with an almighty issue and after sitting on it and thinking it through I thought the sensible and practical thing to do was to tell my Mother about this issue. It was something I thought about a lot and struggled with over two months.

I told my Mother one evening after working in my job on the psychiatric ward. What was her response? Visible shock and then: "did he listen to the rest of the tape?" well he had and as I write this I wish I could go back in

58

time and swiftly intervene. I was then told that I had a sister two years younger (same Father) who was born disabled and had been adopted. Before I really had time to respond she said: "there are other things as well", it was such an open statement. Then she said "your Father raped me..." she then went on to describe in detail how this was done. I am not going to give these details because although it would explain even further the kind of disturbing trauma I had dumped on me it is something so graphic and sick that I don't want to inflict it upon another person. She also told me about the police being involved.

Life Immediately After The Incident -I can only describe the time after this as wandering around in a bubble, really; at times drifting, while at other times floating in an unreality. I was truly by myself and the bubble analogy comes to mind as I was in a state of genuine shock and introspection while everyday life very suddenly felt almost secondary to where I immediately was. On a superficial level I was functioning in the outside world in that my job was going as I wanted it to. My friends had no idea (and still have no idea). But I could not fathom why this information had been given to me.

Finding out I had a disabled sister that was adopted for me was slightly different as coincidentally I'd already worked in this area and for me it wasn't as stigmatised as it might be for the next person. It did contribute significantly to how I was feeling in the initial months following the incident but for me it wasn't as emotionally loaded. This was the kind of family secret that I am sure many siblings never find out about and are oblivious to for a lifetime. Nonetheless I am sure this kind of secret can split families if it somehow spills out many years later like this.

My mind was racing with thoughts and emotions including upset, trauma, deep sadness, anger at both my parents perhaps something beyond that towards my father. It felt so cruel and unnecessary. I started having nightmares including going to the scene of the incident which had been painted in my head which I could not remove. I'd wake up and my heart would be racing and my adrenaline through the roof as I had these confused and disturbing nightmares. "Emotional distance" was the word that came into my head a lot-I didn't have any emotional distance from this incident and it was haunting me. Questions were in my head that I simply could not answer.

I experienced dread, fear, panic while sometimes I'd level out and then I'd hear the word "rape" on the six o'clock news and that would be it-I'd spiral down for hours. For months it was the first thing that came into my head in the morning and the last thing on my mind at night. After about six months I decided I wanted to tell my Mother I was disturbed by what she'd dumped on me-I guess I needed to tell her this to try and move on and I was hoping for some kind of an apology. Her stern response was the false insinuation that it was my fault because "you asked" before following it up with "you'll get over it" she then added seconds later "at least it didn't happen to you". Talk about tough love, I'd call it ugly love.

My Mother's pathetic response marked closure on the six months after the incident. Perhaps she thought that if she did not admit that it was wrong then somehow it would not be. I realised I'd been emotionally crippled since the incident and a quote came into my head from a book I'd read the year before it came from a biography on Neil Young from his album producer David Brigg's philosophy on life. It read simply: "life's a shit sandwich-eat it or die".

I wrote it onto a scrap of paper and when I was getting tangled up in introspection I would look at it and usually it would bring a wry smile. I knew if I remained at this stage I was heading for a slippery slope and the quote seemed to sum up where I was at and it helped me to move forwards.
Away from my personal life I became interested in occupational therapy as a potential career and a job came up on the mental health side around this time. I stumbled through the interview at times and didn't put myself across very well but just about managed to get selected for the job among other applicants.

Recovery to Emancipation - The last thing I was going to do was go to the doctors, which is a typical male response, I know. Through all of this I asked for peace of mind. At night I'd often ask to move onto the next stage and for my mind to rest and that the internal chaos would settle down. I don't know if I was purely speaking to myself through internal dialogue or leaving messages on God's answer phone as I am not religious in the traditional sense. But something kept me going whether it was pure grit or the heavens above.

I would like to tell you that there is a combination of things that can help you in any situation like an emotional toolkit however I have discovered that healing, recovery and emancipation is not an exact science and we cannot take a magic pill or pick-up a particular book that will immediately answer our problems. I believe healing and emancipation is an art and what works for me might not be helpful for the next person. I began looking at outlets for moving on and soon after the conversation with Mother I seriously considered going to a local open mic comedy night I'd heard about and standing up there telling a few dozen strangers my story.

I hadn't come to terms with it, however my perspective was gradually beginning to shift. You can probably guess what my closing punch line would have been 'and then my Mother said "well at least it didn't happen to you" as a consolation' (I raise my eyebrows)...the crowd aren't sure whether to laugh or cry. I shelved the idea but it was food for thought.

Lenny Bruce, Richard Pryor and Bill Hicks are considered great comedians and are personal favourites yet masked behind the laughter they had a serious message and exorcised great pain within them as I discovered through reading their life stories. Bruce was about free speech, common sense and a social critic. Pryor made observations about racism and telling us how it was. Hick's was like a preacher telling us about politics, the insanity of capitalist consumerism and philosophy.

I read a lot about people that inspired me - particularly those who had been through adversity in all kinds of different areas that I admired. This was a breakthrough as I didn't really see the point in reading in my teenage years thinking it was geeky. I found reading self-help and self-improvement books worked as a catalyst at times and other related subjects including books on psychology, Neuro Linguistic Programming and Cognitive Behavioural Therapy. I know that these things aren't to everyone's taste and they weren't always to mine but sometimes they provided a connection, breakthrough, perspective change or some practical inspiration.

Mental well being is the obvious issue here but I have come to believe other perspectives through working in other areas of healthcare. I have worked with people that have been affected through physical and neurological illness. I have seen individuals go through major stress, depression and trauma and I have seen cases of Parkinson's Disease, Cancer and Dementia preceded by emotional trauma.

61

The body and the mind are interconnected and impact on and can influence another. I started exercising regularly and incorporated it into my routine such as cycling to work. I found this helpful particularly when I really didn't fancy doing it as by the end I always felt better than before, purposefully utlilising the physical to alter my emotional state i.e. blasting my brain with oxygen on my bike and making it focus on the road ahead rather than the four walls and an army of introversion.

I continued my lifelong obsession with music by listening to loads as usual, branching out into yet more styles and also learning to play an instrument which was something I'd previously wanted to do but for some reason had not followed-up the idea. The first time I jammed with a group of musicians was something really special.

I made a conscious effort to watch more films as previously I hadn't been that bothered about them and I found that this was generally more inspiring than a lot of the junk that was on television. I also drank less (mainly because I was busy doing other stuff) and I ate a bit healthier. I also embarked upon some travel ambitions which were an interest I had acquired in the last couple of years and fantastic for gaining fresh perspective.

The key thing for me was that I began filtering my intake and consciously occupying myself. I tried to push myself through the bubble and gradually out of my self-imposed comfort zone. Again I highlight that recovery is individual and an art that perhaps each person should discover by realising their own issues, interests and ambitions.

I applied to become an occupational therapist because I liked the philosophy behind the profession and this required going back to university so I moved down to London. I knew I needed the move for lots of reasons; it was truly time for a major change. I was very lucky in that I believe when I was at my lowest work helped me to give back to people which was also a way for me to heal. This move was an all engaging thing which consumed me as I adjusted to the course, life in the capital and a new network of friends.

After battling with it for so long I felt something like an epiphany-a feeling of peace and a clear indication that I was really moving on. It was like sunshine peaking out of a sky full of clouds. The clouds had been covering the horizon for so long I had forgotten how this felt. It appeared only briefly but it was a sign I was not sure would appear at times and ironically it happened in the busy streets of the capital.

Since this happened two years after the incident it has been increasingly reappearing gradually more and more. Shortly after this I re-emerged from the metaphorical bubble I described earlier. I was breaking back into reality and I honestly felt like I had my life handed back to me and this feeling was really something because I know how hard I worked for it. I lived life with a renewed zest and a realisation of how precious it is having felt that it was taken away from me.

How can this be related to a physics class? At secondary school my science teacher told me that you can't create or destroy energy you can only change it and perhaps this universal scientific law can be applied to any other area of life when you think about it.

I want to tell you this-my Mother was wrong. You don't "get over it". Emotional trauma you carry around for life and it changes you. It is that raw energy and how you use it once those initial flames have settled that really defines how you react and what you become. By taking the time to write this I am hoping to achieve something quite incredible. I want to manifest light from something very dark and I want to turn this energy into something bright, beautiful and inspiring. Forget being prime minister or anything else! Surely the most important job in the world if you are a parent is being a source of inspiration for your child. It is not for me to tell anyone how to do anything but surely transferring and dumping issues onto children that cannot be resolved by them is counterproductive.

This is the one thing I thought I could never EVER write a story about and yet it is the first thing I have ever written. It might well be the only thing I put to paper but I have almost done it now. Having read through other peoples stories in this book it again reminds me about perspective and how extraordinary the human spirit can be.

What do I think of my Mother? She has been on anti-depressants for many years and by definition is diagnosed as depressed but it's not really as simple as a label like an illness. I think in her way she did the best for me that she could. In some ways her logic seemed at best skewed (for example telling me repeatedly that I would fail at university while driving me up to Leeds in the car). I do partly consider her a product of the environment that she was raised in which was far from ideal.

My relationship with her is generally improving over time but will probably never be straight forward; there are more boundaries now and it more closely resembles a "normal" relationship. What I would really like is for her to just say "sorry" for the incident. But still I love her even if I carry mixed emotions regarding parenting.

What do I think about my Father? Well quite simply he was never really a Father to me and every time I wrote that word in this story it felt like the wrong word to describe him. I never had a problem with not having a Father around while growing up but the incident brought out a lot of horrible emotions...talk about Mummy and Daddy issues! I don't love you Father but then I don't hate you either I trust that living with yourself is enough retribution.

The future is something I can face up to now and if all goes well I will be a qualified health professional next year. I had the benefit several years ago of attending a "Training for Trainers" course facilitated by Marion which enabled me to learn more about mental health and participate in a group of both service users and healthcare workers with a level dynamic, and it is an experience that will always enlighten and inform my work. Although the opportunity to share my story at the time was too alarming, it set me a personal challenge which two years on I have fulfilled.

As this book informs we are constantly recovering and as we know life is not a smoothly paved path to nowhere. For me personal ambitions are within my grasp now including becoming a qualified health professional next year and I'm going to run the London marathon having worked my way from struggling to run for twenty minutes when I began, I managed the half-marathon earlier this year if I complete the full marathon I will have managed 26 miles and no one is more surprised by this than myself! Perhaps this is also symbolic of my personal journey and how I have gradually progressed. As I write this I feel a sense of relief knowing how far things have moved along from recovery to thriving and emancipating myself.

"Seeing with new eyes" - Marion Aslan

"The real voyage of discovery consists not in seeing new landscapes but in having new eyes" Marcel Proust

Time, Healing, Resilience, Interdependence, Vivacity and Emancipation are the underpinning elements we speak of in "The THRIVE Approach to Wellness"(Aslan & Smith 2007). The narratives in this anthology show how crucial these various components were to the authors in moving on in recovery, and the themes come up quite frequently in each person's story. But maybe one final theme needs to be addressed - that of love. Some years ago, at a conference I attended on Recovery in Mental Health, a tired look- ing service user stood up at the end of the day, and having listened all day to hordes of professionals giving their expert advice on mental ill health ad- dressed the plenary panel. "That's all very well" he said, "but can you love your clients?" He didn't get much of an answer; a deathly silence and a few embarrassed shuffles and throat clearing seemed about the best anyone from the stage could manage, before changing the subject completely.

Love is not a word often heard in mental health spheres, and as we only have one word in English for the emotion it can be misused, misunderstood or abused. But taking just one of the four words which the Greeks used for the emotion - Agape, which is the highest form of love there is, and prob- ably what the gentleman at the conference was referring to, it would seem to me an essential part of healing and moving on in recovery. Agape refers to an unconditional love for others in spite of their character flaws and weaknesses, and love for oneself - which is usually more difficult to achieve.

Around the same time of this conference my son reminded me of the dif- ficulties of showing normal human responses within the medical profes- sion. Watching "Waking the Dead" he responded to my comment that "I couldn't be a coroner, could you?" with a scathing look and the retort to my naivety "Mum, doctors are trained to keep a professional distance and not get emotionally involved"

65

Ah... but what if they did "get involved", "see" the person and care for them as they would a "loved one?" What if mental health service provision was based on how we would wish to see our loved ones (or ourselves!) cared for? Would we still see the need to pump people full of toxic drugs that ultimately may kill or disable them? To label and pathologise pain, distress, human frailty and exposure to abuse? To quote pseudo-science mumble jumble about abstract concepts such as so-called "Schizophrenia" as if it were truly known to what we refer! I do know of many workers who truly care for their clients, who go the extra mile and these are the workers who gain from seeing their clients move on and reclaim their lives as they respond to that care. They are the "miracle workers" - though in reality they are not working miracles, just putting in the hard work and offering love and compassion in the best way they can within a medical orthodoxy, nurturing the person back to wellness!

The true miracle is that many people, despite becoming entrenched in psychiatry with its medicalisation of human life experiences, find it in themselves to recover and thrive. Time, healing and resilience are the cornerstones of this initial part of the journey. In Bethany's chapter, "Stressed, Traumatised and Bewitched" she recalls the miracle her family witnessed, "My mother was the victim of a system, a very powerful system which medicalised her distress and which drove her nearly into the ground. I am glad that she managed to re-frame what was a frightening journey."

It is this fearfulness which comes up time and time again as I work with individuals battered by the system, a concrete fear which I have personal experience of through my own hospitalisations in the past. As a professional, confident woman I was stripped completely of that confidence, my self esteem and my dignity as my sanity was questioned. This and physical assaults by patients and intimidation and coercion regarding medication from staff on the wards left me in a powerless, fearful state of being, though I accept that none of the staff would have deliberately set out to intimidate or frighten me. Fear is induced when power imbalances exist, and once a person is deemed mad they lose all power.

Olga gives a clear account of the way power imbalances are constructed in her chapter, "Emancipation or not" and how our emotional needs are unmet within a system that perpetuates a cycle of false assumptions and negative expectations. Told she would never recover, Olga had to take the power back and emancipate herself, and again the commonality of thriving for her includes love; "I am free, I have love and I am living life to its fullest potential"

Jennifer talks very poignantly about learning to love herself again in her chapter, "We are not born walking" - "Learning to love myself is the easy part, staying in love with myself is a life long journey" Her reflection on our "falling out" with society - "I believe that we all have a falling out with society... holds an allegory for psychiatry. "It is about talking and listening...sharing and forgiving." There is much historically and currently occurring within psychiatric practice that needs forgiveness. Vanessa writes in "My Story" of "the need to get the dirt out of you". She, like many others I have worked with over the last fourteen years is the victim of a range of horrific abuses, traumas and degradation yet she is the one who was labelled with the mental disorder. There is little love or compassion in a psychiatric system and a society which sees the innocent victim who tries to survive their ordeal in whatever way possible as having the disordered personality rather than the perpetrator of the abuse!

As I travel to different parts of the world delivering mental health training and consultancy I am struck by how frequently I hear stories of distress, self healing, recovery and thriving similar to the ones documented in this book. Encouragingly the elements of recovery worldwide are pretty well defined by those of us who have used services or experienced mental distress- we are saying the same things just in different languages. I am also struck by how frequently those of us around the world who dare to speak out against the coercive nature of the medical approach and the damage inflicted within the psychiatric system are marginalised, ignored, ridiculed and derided or our views misrepresented.

People's powerful narratives are often dismissed as "anecdotal evidence" yet it is only when we learn to truly listen to the narratives and to understand the context of distress in people's lives, when we refuse to submit to going down the route of an illness model and reject the notion of "the other" but understand that "there but for the grace of God, go I" that we have a chance to help individuals towards wellness and emancipation. While the issues of power and politics still pervade and often hinder the process, people will have to continue to learn how to emancipate themselves despite psychiatric intervention. We must return hope, not only to the individuals caught up in distress but to the workers themselves who often wish to do things differently, but who themselves are often caught up in a power ridden system. And alongside hope comes love - you may recognise the Biblical quote, "There is no fear in love; but perfect love casts out fear".

Mike Radford in his chapter, "Healing and the handling of uncertainty" describes the fear which pervades services currently. He states, "In order to move from recovery to emancipation, I believe it is necessary to move from the fear which has come to dominate the mental health services in the last ten years." He speaks of "relationships based on trust and equality." Louise echoes this message in her chapter, "Recovery." She writes, "On reflection, recovery for me was about re-establishing equal relationships." I do not personally believe that this is possible without a paradigm shift away from seeing consequences of trauma and distress as symptoms of illness. The challenge is for all of us involved in mental health services or supporting loved ones to see distress with different eyes; "It is with the heart that one sees rightly; what is essential is invisible to the eye." (Antoine de Saint Exupery from The Little Prince)

Daniel, like many others, was very fortunate in avoiding the mental health system completely, "The last thing I was going to do was go to the doctors." He drew on his own resilience and among other things a spiritual love and sustenance from himself or maybe somewhere else for his recovery. "I don't know if I was purely speaking to myself through internal dialogue or leaving messages on God's answer phone as I am not religious in the traditional sense. But something kept me going whether it was pure grit or the heavens above."

Turning points are vital in kick-starting the journey of recovery and thriving, and although the mental health system can be detrimental, there are thankfully many good individual workers who care about their clients and work in very person centred ways. Guy was fortunate in meeting a worker prepared to meet him on a different level and who engaged with him regarding his voices. "Eventually I got moved to an early intervention team. This is where my recovery really began, although at first I didn't care what they had to say as all I wanted was to die. Then I met an occupational therapist on the team who talked to me about the voices". He was enabled to make sense of his voice hearing experience and see it in relation to his life experiences. A loving worker enabled Guy to love and accept himself. "Meditation and confronting my feelings has been a big step in my emancipation, as has learning to accept myself. I no longer see myself as ill or damaged but human. I don't think I'm stupid or worthless anymore. Now I see my "illness" as a reaction to my life experiences and my environment."

Mandy echoes many of the above points in her chapter, "Surviving Abuse". She writes of how emancipation was a slow process as the captor was herself, trapped in a violent relationship. She was fortunate to access loving support from workers at Women's Aid who assisted her in her journey back to wellness. "I've learnt how to love myself as well as loving others and that no situation is really hopeless - there is help out there if you take that first step and ask for it, because "you're worth it. It's not easy, but after a bereavement period we are free to love again; we don't forget but we do move on."

Many people who recover from mental distress choose to use their knowledge and expertise to help others, commonly known as a "survivor mission"- by helping others we learn to help ourselves. Mary Nettle is a fantastic example of such a mission with her services to Survivors Speak Out, Mindlink and ENUSP and her dedication over the years to helping to develop Survivor groups. It is thanks mainly to her, and a wonderful Social worker in Coventry, Jan Turnbull that I found my own survivor mission. Thanks to their encouragement, love and support I was enabled to start working in mental health in a truly meaningful way.

People recover from mental distress. This anthology is a microcosm of Recovery which can and does occur regardless of diagnosis, regardless of the depths of despair to which people plunge and, thankfully, despite the negative messages of "illness" from some quarters. As a child of the 60's I still maintain that optimism for truth, peace and love held by so many wonderful visionaries of the day and the following quote is as applicable to the regime of coercive psychiatry as it is to other regimes around the world. *"When the power of love overcomes the love of power the world will know peace" Jimi Hendrix*